Intervention

Blackline Masters

Level 2

Columbus, OH

Printed in the United States of America.

Send all inquiries to this address:
SRA/McGraw-Hill
4400 Easton Commons
Columbus, OH 43219

ISBN: 978-0-07-610431-4
MHID: 0-07-610431-1

3 4 5 6 7 8 9 COU 13 12 11 10 09 08

The McGraw·Hill Companies

Table of Contents

Intervention Selections

Table of Contents

Table of Contents

Grammar, Usage, and Mechanics

Kindness

Let's Explore

Unit 3

Around the Town

Table of Contents

Gone Fishing 2

by Morris Lindsay 5

Chuck was excited. He was going fishing with his 14
father at the lake. It was his first time ever to fish. 26

When they arrived at the lake, Chuck asked, "What 35
do we do first?" 39

"We get our poles ready," Dad said. 46

Dad took out the poles. First he put a worm on 57
his line. Then he helped with Chuck's line. Then they 67
both cast their poles out into the water. 75

"Now what?" Chuck asked. 79

"We sit and wait," said Dad. 85

The two sat quietly. Soon Chuck felt a pull on 95
his line. 97

"Dad, I got one! I got one!" he cried. "My first fish!" 109

Chuck looked at the fish's face. He thought it 118
looked sad. He felt bad. 123

Chuck put the fish in a pail. The fish jumped a 134
little. Chuck looked at it again. Finally he threw it 144
back in the lake. 148

"Fish, go home," he said. 153

At first Dad looked surprised. Then he smiled. 161

"That was kind of you, son," he said. "Very kind." 171

The Frowning Clown 3

by Sara Stanton 6

A clown named Brownie lived in a big house at 16
the edge of town. He liked his big house, but it was 28
far from town where the other clowns lived. Brownie 37
was lonely. He was so lonely that he spent the day 48
frowning. 49

One day, the clowns from town came to visit 58
Brownie. They tried to make him smile. They 66
squirted water from funny flowers. Some juggled 73
balls high in the air. Others rode their unicycles up 83
and down, waving their arms and tooting their horns. 92
But still they could not make Brownie smile. 100

Then a little clown gave Brownie a big hug. 109

"How can I make you happy?" asked the little 118
clown. "Here, take my hand! I will be your friend. 128
Don't be sad, Brownie. Don't feel left out. We will 138
come to play with you." 143

"You will?" cried Brownie. "Now, I am not sad." 152
He smiled and laughed out loud. Now Brownie no 161
longer frowns. He is a happy clown! 168

The Lion and the Mouse 5

retold by Jane Cummings 9

Once, a mouse ran over a sleeping lion's paw. The 19
lion woke up and grabbed the mouse. 26

"Now, I'll eat you!" the lion cried. 33

The tiny mouse was very frightened. 39

"Don't eat me," the mouse said. "That wouldn't 47
be wise. One day, I may be able to help you," said 59
the mouse. 61

"You are too tiny to help me," the lion said, "but I'll 73
be kind, anyway." And so, the lion let the mouse go. 84

The next day, the mouse heard a cry. She saw the 95
lion trapped in a net. He tried to get out but could not. 108

"Help me! Help me!" the lion cried. 115

The mouse began to bite the net. Soon, there was 125
a wide hole and the lion leaped out. He smiled at the 137
mouse. 138

"You are the kindest friend ever," the lion sighed. 147

"It pays to be nice," said the mouse. 155

A Sweet Treat 3

by Darrell Fish 6

Hen was sitting by a tree. Cow and Bee went over 17
to see her. 20

"I'm hungry," said Hen. "I want to eat something 29
sweet." 30

"Sweeter than cream?" asked Cow. 35

"Sweeter than berries?" asked Bee. 40

"Even sweeter than cherries!" said Hen. "But what 48
might that be?" 51

"I believe I know," said Cow. "You can eat custard." 61

"Where do I get it?" asked Hen. 68

Cow said, "We can make it for you. We need honey, 79
milk, and eggs." 82

"I have honey," said Bee. 87

"I have milk," said Cow. 92

"I have eggs!" cried Hen. 97

Cow and Bee mixed these three foods. They made 106
custard for Hen. What a tasty treat! It was tastier 116
than cheese! 118

"You two are very kind!" said Hen. "Please eat 127
with me." 129

She gave custard to each friend. 135

"You are very kind!" they both said. 142

The Kind King 3

by Molly Wells 6

King Kind ruled the land. 11
His wife, Queen Mean, ruled it too. 18
The king was kind, but the queen was mean. 27
That was a fact that everyone knew. 34

One day King Kind planned a trip. 41
Queen Mean said, "I will go with you!" 49
So, off she went to pack her bag. 57
And what a heavy bag it was, too! 65

Queen Mean flung her bag on the back of a mule. 76
The poor little animal nearly fell to his knees. 85
The mule was used to carrying light loads. 93
He cried, "Take this heavy bag off me, please!" 102

"Move, stubborn mule, move right now! 108
Or I'll kick you as hard as I can," said Queen Mean. 120
But as much as he tried—and he really did try— 131
The poor little mule could not move, it did seem. 141

"Here, let me try," said King Kind. 148
"I don't want the little mule to cry." 156
He petted the mule gently and asked very kindly, 165
"Little mule, won't you at least try?" 172

When the mule heard these words, he began to move, 182
Slowly at first, but then with more speed. 190
Queen Mean was surprised and learned 196
something new: 198
The kinder you are to an animal friend, the more 208
he will do for you! 213

The Amazing Basket 3

by Bill Neder 6

Long ago, a man and his wife met a stranger on 17
the road. 19

"Take this amazing basket," the stranger said. 26
"What goes in one, comes out two." Then he left. 36

The wife put her bow into the basket. Sure enough, 46
out came two bows! 50

Then the man put in his coat. Out came two coats! 61

"What a kind gift!" he cried. 67

The man and his wife took the basket home. They 77
put a roll into the basket. Out came two rolls! 87

"Our bed is small," said the wife. "Let's put it in the 99
basket. Then we'll have two beds." 105

So, the man and his wife tried to push their bed 116
into the basket, but it wouldn't go. It was too big. 127
They pushed and pushed until the basket broke 135
in two. 137

The kind stranger appeared. 141

"Now you know," he said. "If one is kind to you, 152
don't ask for too much." 157

The Fox and the Crow 5

retold by Olivia Green 9

Crow sat in a tree. She was very happy. She had 20
cheese in her mouth. 24

Fox came by. He wanted the cheese. How good 33
it looked! 35

"Hello, Crow," said Fox. "That cheese looks so 43
good. May I please have some?" 49

Crow shook her head, "No." 54

"I am very hungry," Fox thought. "I must have 63
that cheese." 65

Then Fox had an idea. 70

"Oh, Crow," Fox said, "you look so nice. Your 79
wings are so pretty. You are such a pretty bird." 89

Crow liked what Fox said. She smiled. But she 98
didn't give up her cheese. 103

Then Fox said, "Dear Crow! I imagine you sing 112
well too. I hope you will sing for me. Will you?" 123

Crow thought, "I do sing well." She opened her 132
mouth to sing, and out fell the cheese! Fox quickly 142
stole it and ran. 146

"Poor Crow!" Fox cried. "Now you know. Be 154
careful when one speaks kind words. Kind words 162
may just be a trick!" 167

The Toy Princess 3

by Sara Stanton 6

Joy was a dusty doll in a small toy store. She was 18
a princess doll with a beautiful dress and a sparkling 28
crown. Joy had been in the toyshop for a long time. 39

"No one will ever buy you," said Roy, a cowboy 49
doll. "Your dress is old and dirty, and your joints need 60
oil. You don't have a big, fancy hat like I do. And you 73
don't know how to ride a horse!" 80

"That's right," said Troy, the clown doll sitting next 89
to Roy. "No one will want to play with you. You don't 101
have a big red nose like I do. You don't have a silly 114
horn that makes funny noises. And you don't know 123
how to juggle balls in the air!" 130

"Wait a minute!" said a voice from the back of the 141
shelf. "You should not tease Joy. We all know that 151
there is a boy or a girl for every toy." 161

Joy was happy to hear this and hoped that it 171
was true. 173

The next day, a boy came into the toyshop. He 183
looked around at every toy in the store. Finally, he 193
decided which one he wanted to buy. 200

"That princess doll is perfect for my little sister," 209
he said. "Tomorrow is her birthday. She will be so 219
happy to have this royal toy with the beautiful dress 229
and sparkling crown!" 232

A Special Card 3

by Monica Payton 6

It was Jason's birthday. He had gotten lots of 15
birthday cards in the mail. They came from friends 24
and relatives from all over the country. There were 33
funny cards and serious cards. Some cards had 41
beautiful pictures. Others had silly drawings. Some 48
had special wrappings. 51

When his grandma's birthday arrived, Jason 57
wanted to get her a special card. Jason asked his 67
father for some advice. 71

"Why don't you recycle some of your old birthday 80
cards?" Jason's dad suggested. 84

"What does that mean?" asked Jason. 90

"*Recycle* means 'to use again,'" said Jason's dad. 98
"You can create something new from things that have 107
already been used." 110

"Recycling is a good idea," said Jason. "I know. I'll 120
cut out pictures and poems from my old cards. I'll 130
write a special note. Then I'll make a collage to send 141
to Grandma. I'll be careful not to wrinkle the card." 151

Grandma smiled when Jason's gift arrived. "What 158
a wonderful grandson I have! This is the very best 168
birthday present of all!" 172

The Truth About Whales 4

by Rose Rivera 7

Size 8

What is the truth about whales? It's true that they are 19
huge. The blue whale is a large animal. In fact, it is 31
the largest animal in the world. Most other whales 40
are huge, too. 43

Mothers and Babies 46

A little known fact about whales is that they are not 57
cruel. In truth, they are very loving. A mother whale 67
swims with her new baby for a year. She refuses to 78
leave it during that time. A mother will give her life 89
to save her baby. 93

Helping Each Other 96

Whales are kind to each other. When a whale is sick, 107
others help it. They lift it up so it can take breaths 119
of air. 121

A sick whale may swim to a beach. Other whales 131
follow it. They refuse to leave the sick whale alone. 141
Sometimes they all die soon afterwards. 147

Whales have a rule for people: don't bother us, and 157
we won't bother you. Whales look out for each other. 167
That's the truth about whales! 172

Apatosaurus, the Gentle Giant 4

by Michele Lee 7

A long time ago, a big dinosaur walked the Earth. 17
When it walked, the ground shook. All it wanted to 27
do was eat plants. Its name was Apatosaurus. 35

A Description of the Apatosaurus 40

The Apatosaurus was huge. It was almost 85 feet long 50
and weighed from 33 to 38 tons. The Apatosaurus 59
had a long neck and tail. Its head, however, was less 70
than two feet long. It had a tiny brain. 79

How the Apatosaurus Lived 83

The Apatosaurus ate plants. Because of its long 91
neck, it was able to eat leaves from the tall trees. If 103
it was attacked, the Apatosaurus would use its tail 112
for protection. 114

Land or Water Animal? 118

The Apatosaurus had nostrils on the top of its head. 128
Some scientists say it stayed in the water a lot. The 139
nostrils helped the dinosaur to breathe in the water. 148
Other scientists say they found its bones far from the 158
water. Maybe it was both a land and a water animal. 169

Wherever it lived, though, the dinosaur was a 177
gentle giant. 179

Rock Collecting 2

by Carolyn Crimi 5

Have you ever picked up a rock out of the soil just 17
because you liked the way it looked? You might want 27
to become a rock collector. 32

Rocks are a part of nature. You might find rocks 42
by rivers or on the beach. You might even find them 53
along a street in a town. 59

Different kinds of rocks have different features. 66
Some rocks, like limestone, are soft. These rocks 74
break into powder. Others, like quartzite, are hard. 82

Rocks with fossils are prized by serious collectors. 90
These rocks contain the remains or marks from 98
plants and animals that were alive long ago. Fossils 107
turn up in the most surprising places. Keep your eyes 117
open. You might find one too! 123

Rocks are not just for studying. Small rocks can 132
be painted with smiling faces or made to look like 142
tiny mice. Two large rocks might make a nice set of 153
bookends. A giant rock might be just the right size 163
for climbing. 165

So the next time you are walking, you might just 175
find the rock that will make you a rock collector well 186
into the future. 189

The Dinosaur Eggs 3

by T.E. Owens 6

Dinosaurs lived long ago. One kind lived in a 15
desert. One of these dinosaurs wanted to lay eggs, so 25
it made a hole in the sand. The dinosaur put the eggs 37
inside the hole. Then it covered the hole with sand. 47

A wind started to blow. It was strong. It blew and 58
blew. Soon more sand blew over the eggs. As time 68
went by, the eggs went far under the sand. 77

A long, long time went by. There were no more 87
dinosaurs. But there still was a desert, and the 96
eggs were still there. The eggs didn't look like eggs 106
anymore. They had changed. They had turned to 114
stone! 115

Some people came to the desert. They were 123
looking for old things. While they were digging in the 133
sand, the people found the stone eggs. 140

Before that, no one knew how dinosaurs were 148
born. Now they knew. The people had made an 157
exciting discovery! Dinosaurs came from eggs! 163

Language of the Bees 4

by Nina Smiley 7

When you know something, you want to share it. 16
But what if you can't speak or write? You might try 27
doing what bees do. 31

Bees talk, but they say no words. Bees 39
communicate with their bodies. Here's what they do: 47

A worker bee travels far from the hive to find food. 58
The food is called nectar. Nectar is a sweet juice that 69
comes from flowers. The bee finds flowers. It goes 78
from flower to flower to collect nectar. It eats some 88
nectar and carries some home. 93

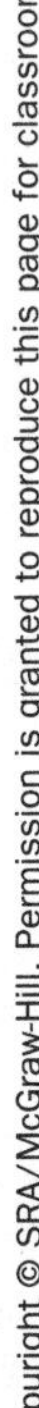

The bee feeds the nectar to other bees, but they 103
want more. How can the bee tell them where it came 114
from? It can't use words. So it uses its body. Bees 125
talk by dancing. The bee zigs and zags. It bobbles 135
and wobbles. It flies in circles. This dance tells the 145
other bees which way to go. It also reveals how far 156
away the flowers are. 160

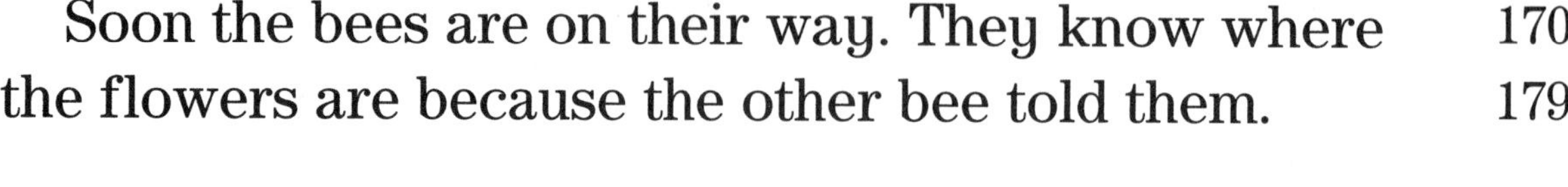

Soon the bees are on their way. They know where 170
the flowers are because the other bee told them. 179

How Do Seeds Travel? 4

by Rosalie Koskimaki 7

Plants have roots, leaves, flowers, and sometimes 14
seeds. New plants grow from seeds. 20

Sometimes seeds fall on the ground around the 28
plants. Then new plants grow next to the old plants. 38

Some plant seeds are as light as feathers. They 47
glide away in the wind. They fall to the ground, and 58
the new plants grow there. 63

Some plants travel with their seeds. The plants quit 72
growing and dry up. The wind pulls them from the 82
ground. They tumble along the ground, dropping off 90
their seeds. 92

Other plants throw their seeds. When these plants 100
are full, they break open. Then the tiny seeds pop out. 111

Other plants grow near the water. Their seeds drop 120
into the water and float away. They may travel miles 130
before they settle into the riverbank. 136

Stickers on some seeds help them travel. These 144
seeds wait for an animal to walk by, and they stick 155
onto its fur. These seeds get a free ride. 164

Wind, water, and animals help spread seeds. Some 172
seeds end up miles away from where they started. 181
These seeds take root and grow into plants in new 191
places. 192

Home, Tweet Home 3

by Steven Soto 6

In the spring, birds begin to make nests. They need 16
a safe place to lay their eggs. It takes time to make a 29
nest, and birds work hard to gather what they need. 39
You can help! 42

After you brush your pet, keep its hair. Birds will 52
use the hair to build their nests. You can even collect 63
hair from your own brush or comb. 70

Short lengths of string and yarn can be used for 80
birds' nests. Make sure the pieces are no more than 90
six inches long. A bird could become ensnared in a 100
long piece of string. Cut scraps of cloth into thin strips 111
for the birds. Birds will also use shredded paper. 120

Birds use things from nature too. They construct 128
nests with twigs from trees and pine needles. They 137
use moss and strips of bark. Dead leaves and dry 147
grass might be part of a nest. 154

The next time you clean your house or yard, think 164
of the birds. Do you have some things they could use? 175

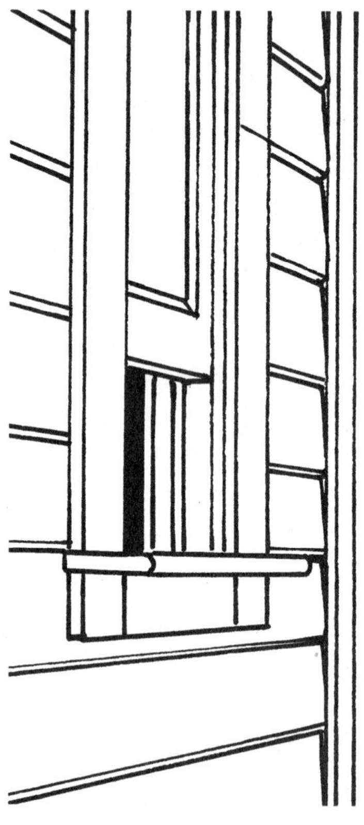

What Is It? 3

by Rosalie Koskimaki 6

"What is it?" Simone asked her father. She showed 15
him the tiny egg. "I found it in the yard," she said. 27

"We'll let it be a surprise," her father said. "Let's put 38
the egg in a jar and wait." 45

One day a worm came out of the egg. 54

Simone ran to her father. "I know what it is," she 65
told him. "It's a worm egg." 71

"Well, it could be a worm egg," said her father, "but 82
let's wait some more." 86

So Simone did. And the worm grew. 93

One day she saw the worm wrapped in a white 103
blanket. 104

"What is that white thing?" Simone asked her 112
father. 113

"That is a cocoon," he said. 119

One day she saw the cocoon moving. Then 127
something started coming out of the cocoon. Soon 135
Simone could see a pretty butterfly. 141

Simone knew what kind of egg she had found! 150

"The caterpillar hatched from the egg," said 157
Simone's father. "Then it built the cocoon. The 165
cocoon protected the caterpillar as it transformed 172
into a butterfly." 175

Simone set the butterfly free. She and her father 184
watched as it fluttered to the sky. 191

Meg's Summer on the Farm 5

by Stephanie Windsor 8

Meg loves to take pictures. She takes her camera 17
on every trip. 20

Last summer, Meg went to her grandpa's farm. She 29
took her camera. She took lots of pictures. 37

Meg started to take pictures as soon as she got to 48
the farm. She took pictures of her grandpa feeding 57
the pigs. 59

Meg took pictures of Max the dog. He was chasing 69
a squirrel. "Silly dog," Meg called to Max. She took 79
another picture of him. 83

Meg's cousins were playing in the hay. They were 92
having a great time! She took a picture of them too. 103
Meg took pictures all over the farm. 110

Meg took pictures of the goats. She took pictures 119
of the kittens under the porch. She even took 128
pictures of the water pump! 133

Meg took pictures of her mother cooking. Then 141
she took pictures of the peach pie her mother had 151
made. Meg surprised her grandpa as he took a bite of 162
pie. She took his picture. 167

"What are you going to do with all your pictures?" 177
Grandpa asked. 179

"I will put them in a book I am going to write," said 192
Meg. "I'll call it *Meg's Summer on the Farm*!" 201

A Winter Bouquet 3

by Judy Ermert 6

Amy liked flowers. In the spring, the garden was 15
pretty. It made Amy happy. 20

But it was winter now. No flowers grew in the 30
garden. 31

Amy was sad. She looked at the garden. It was 41
empty. Where had the violets been? Oh yes, under 50
the tree. Grandma liked the violets best. 57

Then Mom had an idea. "Let's wake up those 66
violets," she said. She got a jar with a lid. She sent 78
Amy to get a spade. They dug up the frozen soil and 90
found seeds. 92

They put the seeds and soil into the jar. Amy added 103
water. They put the lid on and placed the jar on the 115
windowsill. 116

"Don't take off the lid," Mom said. "The sunshine 125
will bring up the water from the soil. The lid will 136
keep the water inside and cause it to rain on the 147
seeds. This will force them to grow." 154

Amy looked at the jar each day. Soon she saw 164
little green sprouts. Up toward the jar lid they 173
stretched. 174

She carried her winter bouquet to her grandma. 182
Grandma was shocked. "How fancy!" she said, 189
"Violets in the winter!" 193

Tracks in the Dirt 4

by Sara Stanton 7

Pete and Lee were camping with Gramps. They 15
spied some marks in the dirt. 21

"Look! Deer tracks," said Lee. "Let's see where they 30
go. May we follow them, Gramps?" 36

"Don't hike too far," said Gramps. "You'll be late 45
for lunch." 47

Pete and Lee grabbed the horn to signal Gramps 56
and a full canteen to use in case they were thirsty. 67

"Don't fret, Gramps," said Pete. "We know the rules." 76

The children hiked and hiked, but no deer appeared. 85

On the trail they came across a black snake, two 95
chipmunks, three puny spiders in a web, a green frog 105
with spots, a smelly skunk, and a slow snail in its 116
shell. But they did not see a single deer. 125

"It's time to turn back," said Pete. "It's getting late. 135
No deer today. Gramps will be sad." 142

The children hiked back to camp. But what a 151
surprise they had. There were deer in the camp! 160

"Look who dropped in for lunch!" said Gramps. 168

My Sister Abby 3

by Jamie Greene 6

"May I turn on the siren now?" 13

"Not now, Zoe. People will think it's an emergency 22
and drive out of our way. We don't want to cause any 34
problems." 35

"Please? It's so exciting to hear the siren's wail!" 44

"Maybe you can use the siren when we get to the 55
hospital parking lot. It shouldn't cause too much 63
trouble there." 65

"Thanks, sis!" 67

See that girl driving the ambulance? That's my big 76
sister, Abby. She's a paramedic. When people are sick 85
or need help, she drives them to the hospital so they 96
can get better. 99

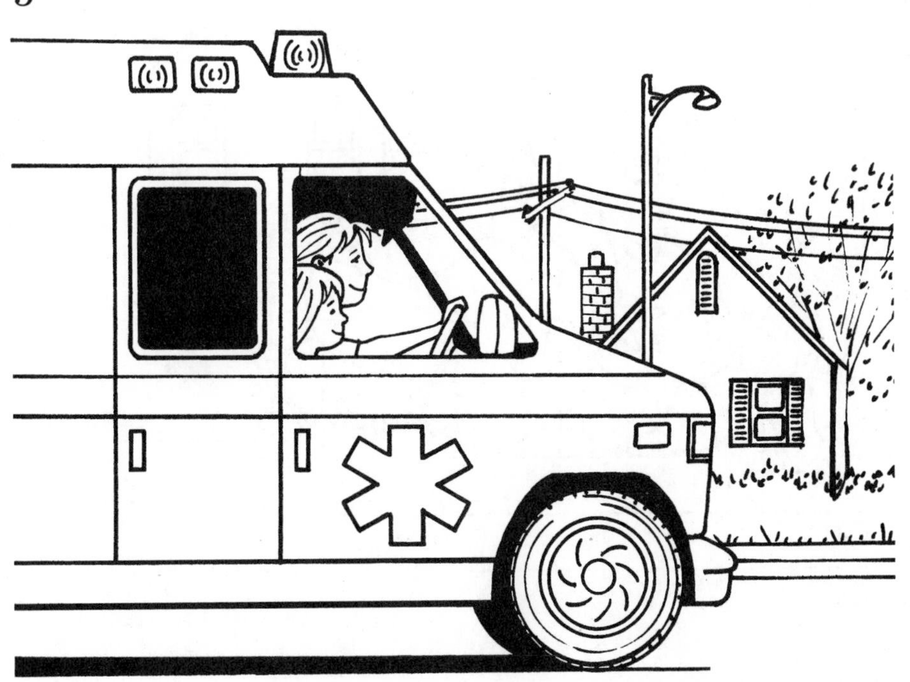

I am sitting next to her. My name is Zoe, and I'm in 112
third grade. I'm working on a project for class, and 122
Abby let me ride in the ambulance with her tonight. 132

So far we have helped a boy who fell off his 143
bicycle, an old man who hurt his knee, and a woman 154
who bumped her elbow. 158

A paramedic's work is never boring because you 166
don't know when or where people will need your 175
help. Abby knows all of the streets in our town, so 186
she can quickly drive anywhere. 191

I always feel safe in my town because I know 201
Abby and the other paramedics are only a phone call 211
away. Their job is to help people, and that makes 221
Abby a hero. 224

The Bus Ride 3

by Tristan Horrom 6

Joe and his mom were going downtown. Joe was 15
excited. He had never been downtown before. 22

They stood at the bus stop and waited for the bus. 33
When the big gray bus pulled up, Joe and his mom 44
climbed on. 46

Joe sat by the window. He stared out as the bus 57
drove through the city. Joe saw people walking on 66
the sidewalk. He saw many shops with brightly lit 75
signs and streets full of cars. Joe had never seen so 86
many new things before! 90

Joe pointed excitedly as the bus drove by a big 100
stone statue. “Look at that, Mom!” he exclaimed. 108
Next the bus went by a tall glass skyscraper. He had 119
not known that buildings could be that huge. Then 128
the bus rolled to a stop outside a big building. A few 140
people got off the bus. Joe saw a sign on the building 152
that read “City Hall.” 156

“That’s where the mayor works,” his mom said. 164

The bus continued through the city. Joe had his 173
face pressed to the window the entire time. The bus 183
stopped at a park downtown. Joe and his mom got 193
off, and Joe thanked the bus driver for the ride. He 204
couldn’t wait to ride the bus back home and see 214
more of the city! 218

My Most Precious Things 4

by Giulia Verzariu 7

"Hi, Sophie!" Uncle Bill says as Mom and I walk 17
into the bank. 20

"Hi, Uncle Bill!" I reply. 25

Uncle Bill is the manager of the bank. On 34
Saturdays, when Mom and I come into town, we go 44
to the bank to see Uncle Bill. 51

"Are you ready to see your deposit box?" he asks. 61

"I'm ready!" 63

Mom, Uncle Bill, and I walk downstairs to the vault. 73

"This is my niece, Sophie," Uncle Bill tells the 82
guard. "She is here to open box number 723." 91

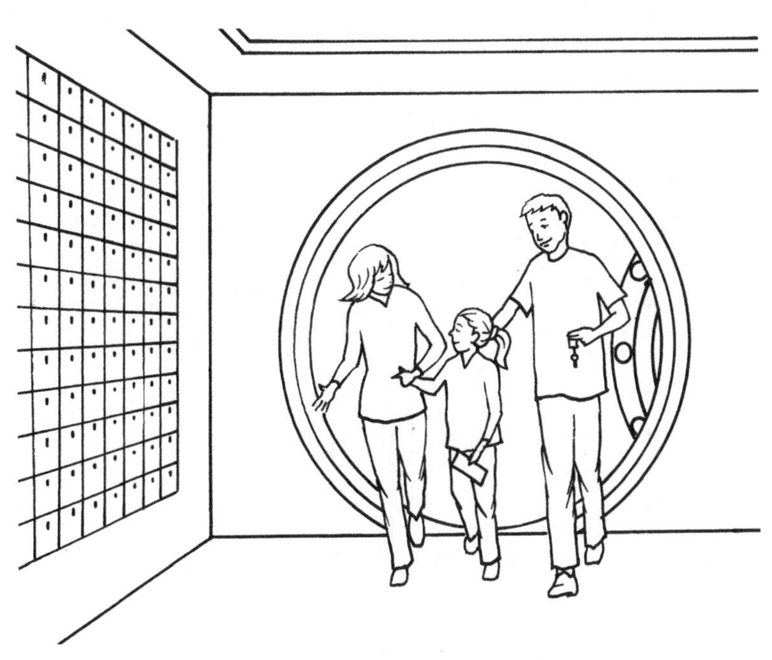

"Right this way, Sophie," says the guard as he 100
leads us into the vault. The walls inside the vault are 111
covered with rows of small locked doors. 118

"Do you have your key?" Mom asks. 125

"Right here!" I tell her as I excitedly pull it out of 137
my pocket. 139

After unlocking the box, the guard takes it out of 149
the wall and puts it in front of me. 158

"Here is box number 723," he says. 165

Inside are my most precious things: my birth 173
certificate, my grandmother's earrings, and my 179
mother's ring. 181

After looking at my things, I reach into my pocket 191
for something else I want to put into the box: my 202
report card. 204

"Wow! Straight A's!" says Uncle Bill. 210

"I just want to make sure this stays safe too!" I say. 222

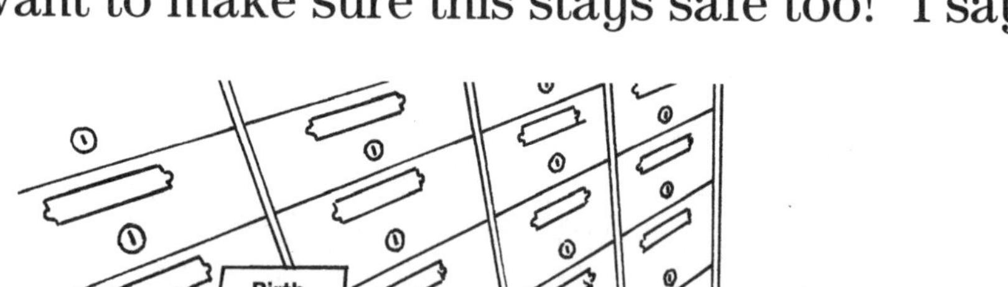

Aisle 3 2

by Irene Martinez 5

Aisle 3 in the grocery store has the best stuff. It 16
has baseball cards and football cards. It has books, 25
toys, juice, and snacks. I talk to Cindy when we go to 37
the store. Cindy is an employee at the grocery store. 47

Cindy stocks the shelves in Aisle 3. She helps 56
unload the trucks that come from the warehouses. 64
She fills up carts and puts new things away. 73

"Do you get tired from picking up so many boxes?" 83
I asked Cindy one day. 88

"Sometimes my back hurts," she said. "So I try to 98
bend from my knees." Cindy works hard. Aisle 3 109
is long. 110

"What do you like the best in Aisle 3?" I asked 121
Cindy. 122

"The books, of course," she said. "Sometimes a 130
book looks so good I have to buy it!" 139

"I like the grape juice the best," I told Cindy. "I 150
have to be careful not to spill it on the floor though," 162
I said. 164

Cindy laughed and pointed. "You need to go to Aisle 174
7," she said. "That's where the carpet cleaner is!" 183

The Bread Shop 3

by Sara Stanton 6

Frank is opening a bread shop on the town square. 16
He will serve warm, fresh bread. Frank will make the 26
bread from scratch. He will use a blend of grains. 36

His bread will be warmer and fresher than any 45
you have tried. His bread will be the warmest and 55
freshest on the block. Frank works hard to make 64
sure his bread is delicious. 69

Best of all, Frank's bread will come in many 78
shapes—a slim slab, a split loaf, or a striped twist. 89
Frank's bread will look different, but each loaf will 98
taste yummy. 100

Some of his breads will be sweet and fluffy. Some 110
breads will be small and spicy. Some will be crunchy 120
and filled with nuts. Some breads will have a hard 130
crust. 131

Some breads will be spread with butter, jam, or 140
jelly. All of them will be tasty and worth the price. 151
Customers will want to try each loaf of bread that 161
Frank bakes. 163

What? You don't like warm bread spread with jam? 172
You don't want tasty bread filled with nuts? Don't 181
worry! Frank also serves the coldest, freshest milk 189
on the street. 192

A Dog for Liz 4

by Paul Cruz 7

Liz walked through the local animal shelter. There 15
were cages of dogs in all sizes. "How do I choose?" 26
she asked her mother. 30

"Well, let's try," her mother answered. 36

A shelter volunteer approached Liz. "My name is 44
Sara," she said. "May I help you find a dog?" 54

"We can't decide! They are all so cute," said Liz's 64
mother. 65

Sara pointed to a small dog. "This dog has lots of 76
energy," she said. "He will be able to jump high. Do 87
you have a tall fence?" 92

"No, we have a short fence," Liz said. 100

Next Sara pointed to a big dog. “This dog will need 111
to go for lots of walks,” she said. “Will you have time 123
to take her?” 126

Liz thought about soccer. Her season was about to 135
begin. “I don’t have much time,” she said. 143

“But we have lots of love,” said Liz’s mother. 152

“I think I have just the dog for you!” Sara said. 163

Sara showed Liz a yellow dog. He had a droopy 173
face and wagging tail. “Buff is five years old,” she 183
said. “Buff doesn’t need a tall fence or long walks. He 194
just needs love.” 197

Liz gave Buff a big hug. Buff licked her face and 208
wagged his tail. 211

“I think we found a dog for Liz,” her mother said. 222
“Thank you, Sara!” 225

City Girl 2

by Dennis Andersen 5

Letter for Eve 8

One day, Eve received a letter. 14

Dear Eve, 16
We miss you. 19
Please come and 22
visit us on our farm. 27
Hugs and kisses, 30
Steve and Lee 33

"I can't leave the city, Mommy!" Eve complained. 41

"You'll have fun on Steve and Lee's farm," said 50
Eve's mom. 52

But Eve still was not sure she wanted to visit the 63
farm. 64

"I'll have a yummy apple. Then I'll feel better," 73
Eve said. 75

But the apple did not make Eve feel better. 84

Steve and Lee met Eve at the train. 92

“We are very happy you are here!” beamed Steve. 101

“You are a city girl now, but you can be a farm girl, 114
too,” added Lee. 117

Eve wasn’t so sure. 121

“This is our farm,” said Steve. “Let’s feed these 130
geese.” 131

Eve peeked at the geese. “I do not like geese,” she 142
whispered. 143

“The farm is busy in the day, and it’s busy after 154
dark!” said Steve. 157

Just then, Eve saw a deer. “What is it?” she asked. 168

“Shhh!” whispered Steve. “See the deer leap?” 175

“Wow! Deer do not leap in the city!” said Eve. 185

“Do you like being on the farm?” asked Steve. 194

“Oh, yes.” said Eve. “It is very pretty.” 202

Dear Mom, 204
Please do not 207
pick me up in a 212
week. 213
The city is pretty, 217
but I like the 221
farm, too. 223
Hugs and kisses, 226
Eve 227

A Trip to the Fire Station 6

by Marcus Reese 9

A big fire truck rolled down the street. Its 18
sirens screamed. Ben watched. He wanted to be a 27
firefighter someday. 29

The next day, Ben's dad took him to the fire 39
station. Ben met a firefighter named John. John 47
showed Ben different kinds of trucks. "This is a 56
ladder truck," said John. "Its ladders can reach tall 65
windows." 66

"How about this truck?" Ben asked. 72

"That's a pumper truck," said John. "It's used to 81
carry water to the fires." 86

Ben looked at John's tools. "Our tools rescue 94
people," explained John. 97

Then John took Ben inside the station. “Firefighters 105
work for twenty-four hours at a time,” he said. “This 116
is where we sleep until someone needs us.” 124

Ben looked at the beds lined up in a row. 134

“Does the fire alarm wake you up?” he asked. 143

“Yes! Then we jump into our trucks!” said John. 152

“Do you get to eat?” Ben asked. 159

“We eat good food,” answered John. “One of 167
the firefighters is our cook. He makes a list, goes 177
shopping, and cooks our meals.” 182

“What happens if the alarm sounds during dinner?” 190
Ben asked. 192

“We quickly jump into our trucks,” John answered. 200

“I have one more question,” said Ben. “May I turn 210
on the siren before I go?” 216

John smiled as he lifted Ben into a shiny new fire 227
truck. 228

Shhhhh! 1

by Anna Reyes 4

Have you ever noticed the librarian at your 12
library? He or she is usually working very hard. 21

What do librarians do? They check books out 29
to people. They put books back on the tall library 39
shelves. They can find you a good story to read. But 50
that's not all that librarians do. Read on! 58

Librarians organize books. They put them in order 66
so they are easy to find. Librarians make catalogs. 75
These are lists for tracking all the books in the 85
library. Librarians also help people use the library's 93
computers. If you have a question, a librarian is there 103
to answer it. 106

Different kinds of librarians do different things. 113
Some buy books for the library. Some help people 122
find facts and information. Others work only with 130
children. These librarians run story hours. They 137
teach children how to use the library. 144

Some librarians work at school libraries. Some 151
work at college libraries. Some work at city libraries. 160
Even large offices need librarians. 165

If you want to find out more about a librarian's job, 176
then talk to a librarian when you can. Find out what 187
he or she does. But be very quiet! 195

My Map 2

by Robert Holmes 5

I made a map of my neighborhood to send to 15
Gram. She hasn't seen our new house yet. My map 25
will help her know how to find it. 33

I put a red *X* on my house on Robin Lane. I put 46
blue *X*s on my friends' Joe and Calli's houses. I drew 57
Mrs. Cohen's house. She lives across the street. She 66
bakes the best molasses muffins I've ever tasted. 74

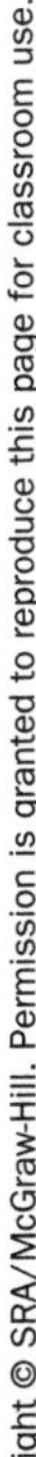

The fire station is on Fox Street. I made another 84
red *X* on my map for it. 91

There's a library and a post office on Fox Street, 101
too. I made green *X*s on the map for them. I drew 113
books by the library. I put a flag by the post office. 125

There's a big pond on Water Street, so I drew the 136
pond right on my map. I made fish jumping out of 147
the water. When Gram gets here, I'm going to take 157
her fishing. 159

I think I'll write a letter to Gram. I'll put my map in 172
the letter. My letter will read: 178

Dear Gram, 180
I miss you. When 184
are you going to visit? 189
I drew a map for you. 195
When you get here, we'll 200
take a long walk. 204
Love, 205
Max 206

I think Gram will write me back and say she's 216
coming next week. 219

A Tricky Spider 3

by Pam Bliss 6

A tiny bug walks along the ground in the woods. 16
Then the bug is gone! What happened? 23

The bug walked by the home of a trap-door spider. 34
The bug was careless. It did not see the spider. The 45
spider was hiding in its home. 51

A trap-door spider digs a hole in the ground to live 63
in. It lines the hole with the silk it spins and loops 75
from its body. Next it covers the hole with a lid. The 87
lid looks like a roof but opens just like a door. It is 100
very useful. 102

The spider waits in its hole for a bug to come along. 114
Bugs are food for the spider. When a bug comes by, 125
the spider opens the lid. It grabs the bug. It drags the 137
bug back into the hole. The spider also uses the hole 148
to keep safe. The spider can hold the lid shut if an 160
animal tries to get in. 165

Would you like to see a trap-door spider? That may 176
be hard. You can look and look. But unless you are a 188
bug walking by, you may never get to see one. 198

Insects Stay Safe 3

by Helen Squires 6

Many insects can stay safe—even when they 14
are out in the open. Do you know any of the tricks 26
insects use to stay safe? 31

Have you heard about the tiny stick that walks? 40
It's not made of wood. It is a small insect called a 52
walking stick. 54

Most walking sticks are as long as your finger. 63
But they're not as wide. They have long, spindly legs. 73
They look like small sticks! Isn't that cool? 81

Birds like to eat the walking stick. But it tricks 91
them. It sits still for a long time to avoid getting 102
caught. The birds think it's a stick. So the birds do 113
not eat it. 116

That's the trick of the walking stick. 123

Another tricky insect is the moth. Some moths 131
have special "eyes" for staying safe. 137

These moths have large spots on their wings. 145
These spots look like owl eyes. When an enemy 154
comes near, the moth lifts its front wings and shows 164
its "eyes." Then suddenly, boo! The enemy is startled 173
and leaves the moth alone. 178

Now that you know some of their tricks, maybe 187
soon you will be able to spot these insects. But you'll 198
have to look hard! 202

The Wise Owl 3

by Christina Widener 6

A wise owl spent most of her time busily looking 16
for mice to eat. The owl would refuse to talk to the 28
other animals when she was hunting. Owl thought it 37
was smarter to work than play. So when her friends 47
would ask her to play Owl would say, "You go ahead 58
and play. I have a lot of work to do. And I don't need 72
you bothering me." Then she would disappear. She 80
would always hide when she was busy. 87

"Owl, don't you want to try some of my new 97
honey?" Bee would ask. 101

"No, no," Owl would say, "I'm way too busy." 110

"Owl, don't you want to look at the pretty sunset?" 120
asked Deer. 122

"No, Deer, I'm too busy," said Owl. 129

One day, Owl noticed that none of her friends were 139
bothering her anymore. 142

"They must think I'm too busy," thought Owl. This 151
made Owl sad. 154

When Owl saw Deer and Bee she asked them, 163
"Hello friends, do you want to come with me on my 174
hunt?" 175

"No," they said, "We're too busy." 181

Owl decided she would no longer hide from her 190
friends when she was busy. Instead she would invite 199
them to help her. Now that was a wise decision. 209

Hide-and-Seek Animals 4

by Shirley Granahan 7

How Do Animals Stay Safe? 12

Animals try to be safe. Why? Here's a clue: other 22
animals want to eat them. Some animals eat only 31
plants. But many animals eat other animals. Owls eat 40
mice. Bears eat fish. So animals have special ways to 50
help themselves stay safe. 54

Some animals use their feet to scratch their 62
enemies. A few use their sharp teeth. Some animals 71
use horns. A skunk gives off a bad smell. And 81
geese bite! 83

The way some animals look helps them stay safe. 92
The shapes and colors of the animals help them hide 102
from their enemies. 105

The Walking Stick 108

Can you find the bug in this picture? It is called a 120
walking stick. It is hiding because a bird came too 130
close. The bug sits still. It looks like a stick. So the 142
bird does not eat it. 147

The Rabbit 149

This rabbit's color helps it hide. Its fur is brown most 160
of the year. The rabbit hides in fields of dry grass. In 172
winter, the rabbit's fur turns white. Then the animal 181
can hide in snow. 185

The Giraffe 187

The giraffe is the same color as the grass around it. 198
Its spots look like shadows from tall trees. A giraffe 208
eats plants. But a lion eats meat. So spots help the 219
giraffe hide from the lion. 224

Name That Color 3

by Hector Garcia 6

What colors are animals? Sometimes their names 13
tell you. But don't always count on it. 21

The Blue Whale 24

The blue whale's color is blue. But some blue whales 34
are also partly yellow. Yellow plants grow on their 43
bellies. 44

The Yellow Jacket 47

Do you know about the yellow jacket? It looks like 57
most bees. It is mostly yellow. But the yellow jacket 67
also has black lines. 71

The Brown Cow 74

"How now, brown cow?" is an old saying. But don't 84
think all cows are brown. Some cows are red, black, 94
white, or gray. Only their milk is always white! 103

The Red Fox 106

Do you know about the red fox? Yes, its fur is red, 118
but not all over. Its belly is white. So is the tip of its 132
tail. And its legs are black. Other red foxes aren't red 143
at all! They are black, gray, or silver. How about that! 154

Brown Bears and Black Bears 159

Have you seen any big brown bears around? They 168
are really big! But they are not always brown. Some 178
big brown bears are yellow or black like soot. 187

What do you know about black bears? They are 196
not just black. Some have white spots and a brown 206
nose. And some black bears are mostly white! 214

Can you know an animal's color by its name? 223
Look again! 225

Uncle Diego's Owl 3

by Isaac Sharit 6

Lina loved to go to the park to swing and fish. 17

One spring day Ranger Jane was helping Lina bait 26
her hook as usual. "The blue gills are biting today," 36
Jane said. Lina reeled in fish after fish. Ranger Jane 46
kept count. 48

Lina's uncle Diego looked up in the trees. He loved 58
to watch birds. He liked red birds. He liked blue 68
birds. He liked ducks. But most of all he loved owls. 79

Lina knew a lot about owls. She knew they came 89
out at night. "You can't see owls in the daytime," 99
Lina said. 101

"I know, I know," said Uncle Diego. "I'd give 110
anything to see an owl at night!" 117

Ranger Jane heard the two talking. "We're going to 126
have a night walk next week," she said. "Why don't 136
you come and bring Lina?" 141

Lina and Uncle Diego got to the park just before 151
dark. Ranger Jane led them on the walk. The park 161
felt different at night. The moon cast a strange 170
shadow over the pond. "I don't think we're going to 180
see an owl," she told her uncle. 187

Whoo! Whoo! came a call from above. Big wings 196
went *woosh, woosh* over Lina's head. "It's your owl, 205
Uncle Diego! It's your owl!" whispered Lina. 212

Ranger Jane laughed. "I think you'll be back for 221
more night walks," she said. 226

"Yes, indeed," said Uncle Diego. 231

Keen on Green 3

by Jorge Cardona 6

The color of an animal can help it hide. Some hide 17
when they are hunting, and some hide to stay safe 27
from hunters. A tree frog does both. 34

There are many kinds of tree frogs. Some have 43
green skin. This helps them blend in with a tree's 53
green leaves. 55

A tree frog has round suction cups on its feet. The 66
frog climbs a tree and tucks itself into a leaf. 76

An insect lands on a crisp leaf. The insect starts 86
to eat. It does not see the green frog on the leaf. 98
Then . . . *snap!* The frog flicks out its tongue and eats 108
the insect. 110

The frog snatches insects off leaves. It grabs bugs 119
from the air. Its quick tongue, which is sticky like 129
glue, shoots out and in. 134

How else does a tree frog use its color? Some tree 145
frogs have bright blue stripes on their legs. They also 155
have bold red eyes and feet. 161

When the frog sleeps, it tucks in its legs and shuts 172
its eyes. The tree frog looks like part of a leaf. 183

But if a predator spies the frog, it wakes up and its 195
red eyes pop open. Its bright blue legs expand as it 206
jumps. The flash of color is a surprise to the hunter. 217
The predator might pause. In the blink of an eye, the 228
frog escapes. 230

Opossums 1

by Rosalie Koskimaki 4

Steve often goes to the woods to play and look 14
around. He tiptoes quietly and keeps a look out for 24
neat animals. Sometimes Steve learns about animals 31
by watching them in the woods. Steve is excited 40
because today he found a place where opossums 48
live. Then he hid behind a tree. He watched the 58
opossums play. 60

The opossums are as big as cats. They are blue- 70
gray with white faces. They have black eyes and 79
ears. They have long, pointed noses and sharp teeth 88
for chewing. 90

Steve watches them climb. Climbing is easy 97
for opossums. Their feet have five toes. One toe 106
resembles a thumb. They use their feet like hands. 115
Their tails help too. Their tails are long and thin. 125
Opossums can hold things in their tails and can climb 135
with their tails. 138

Opossums are most famous for playing dead. 145
Some animals eat opossums, but very few will 153
bother a dead opossum. So when an enemy comes 162
along, opossums play dead. They lie down and shut 171
their eyes. They don't move. They look dead. Soon 180
the enemy goes away. Steve knows that is how 189
opossums stay safe. He thinks it is a clever way to 200
escape danger. 202

Frogs and Toads 3

by George Johnson 6

Have you seen frogs and toads? They may look 15
the same to you, but look again. Frogs and toads are 26
different. Do you know why? 31

Shape, Skin, Legs 34

First look at their shapes. A toad is flatter than a 45
frog. A frog is rounder than a toad. Also, a toad is 57
wider. 58

Now look at their skin. A toad has dry skin. A frog 70
has thin, wet skin. A toad's skin also has small bumps 81
on it. The bumps are called warts. A frog has no 92
warts. Its skin is smooth. 97

Frogs have strong back legs. They can leap far. 106
Toads can't leap as far. Why? Because their back legs 116
are not as strong. 120

Water and Land 123

Both frogs and toads are found in water. Maybe you 133
once saw them in a pond. Both can live in water or 145
on land. But they are not the same. 153

Toads grow up in water. Soon they are big. Then 163
they stay on land. They only return to ponds to lay 174
their eggs. 176

Some frogs stay in water all the time. Some frogs 186
stay on land all the time. Others stay on land most of 198
the time. They go to ponds only to lay their eggs. 209

You may have thought frogs and toads are the 218
same. Now you know they are different. 225

Oh, Deer! 2

by Mary Ramos 5

Animals are most at risk when they are young 14
babies. They are weak, small, and slow. How do they 24
survive? The color of their skin and fur helps them. 34

A fawn is a baby deer. It can walk when it is born, 47
but it cannot run fast. It needs help staying safe. That 58
is why a fawn has brown fur with white spots. 68

Brown is the color of the forest floor. When sun 78
shines through the trees, it creates bright spots on 87
the ground. When a fawn lies down in the forest, it 98
blends in. This helps keep the fawn safe. 106

There are times a doe, or mother deer, must leave 116
her fawn. When the fawn is alone, it lies still and 127
stretches out its neck. The fawn stays flat on the 137
ground. It is hard for enemies to see the fawn. 147

As the fawn grows, it gets stronger and can run 157
faster. It has a better chance to escape harm. The 167
fawn's spots fade. 170

But grown deer need protection too. Their coats 178
help them blend in with the woods and tall grass 188
where they live. Does and bucks, or female and male 198
deer, have a tan or brown coat in the summer. 208

In the winter, color fades from many plants. The 217
deer's fur changes color too. Their coats look more 226
gray than brown. Now they can blend in once more. 236

The Dragon Who Was Afraid 5

by Taisha Brown 8

Once there was a dragon who was afraid. 16
He feared everyone and everything in the forest 24
without cause. But mainly he was afraid of 32
the dark. 34

Late one day, the dragon was racing through 42
the forest. 44

"Why are you racing?" a voice asked. 51

The dragon stopped and turned around. He looked 59
up, down, left, and right. Yet he saw no one. 69

"That's very strange," the dragon thought. "I must 77
be imagining things." 80

"Wait, I'm in the grass!" the voice shouted. 88

The dragon looked down and saw a tiny ant. He 98
jumped back. 100

"Eek, an ant!" he cried. 105

"I can't harm you," the ant said. "You're big, and I'm 116
small. Why are you afraid?" 121

"Because it's late," the dragon said. "It's becoming 129
dark, and I'm afraid of everything in the dark." 138

"But you're a dragon," the ant said. "You can 147
breathe fire." 149

"I can?" the dragon asked. 154

"Yes," the ant said. "Use your fire to see in the dark." 166

The dragon took a breath and blew. What a huge 176
fire he made! 179

"I can see!" the dragon cried. "Thank you, ant! Now 189
I'll never fear anything again!" And he never did! 198

The World's Bravest Cowboy 4

by Jake Barnes 7

Have you ever heard of Pecos Bill? Some people 16
believe he was the bravest cowboy who ever lived. 25
Except he never really lived. He's a made-up person 35
with a lot of stories told about him. 43

Pecos Bill Takes on Wild Animals 49

One of the stories is about Bill's fight with a snake. 60
The snake got to Bill first. But Bill did not yield. 71
Because he held the snake tight, its face turned 80
bright red. That snake hurried away fast! 87

Another time, a mountain lion was hiding in a field. 97
With jaws open, it leaped on Bill's back and hit him 108
with its paws. But Bill jumped on the lion's back! Bill 119
rode that lion down a long road! 126

Pecos Bill Rides a Cyclone 131

One time he said that he could ride a cyclone. 141
Friends thought the strong wind would throw Bill 149
to the ground, but they were wrong. The cyclone 158
carried Bill all over the state! At last the cyclone 168
gave up and turned to rain. It was the only way to 180
get Bill off the cyclone's top! 186

Real or Make-Believe? 190

How did Pecos Bill get to be so brave? Some say he 202
fell out of his family's wagon as a child. He became 213
lost and was raised by wolves. Is that too hard to 224
believe? Just remember, Pecos Bill stories are all 232
make-believe! 234

Faith as a Friend 4

by Marjorie Abson 7

Faith was on her way to school when she saw Paige. 18

"Oh, no," Faith thought. "Here comes that girl." 26

"Whose jacket are you wearing?" Paige asked. "It 34
looks very old. I like to wear new clothes. My friends 45
all wear new clothes." 49

Faith's mom wore the jacket when she was Faith's 58
age, and Faith really liked it. She didn't know what to 69
say to Paige, so she just kept walking. 77

The time came for gym class. Suddenly, Faith 85
tripped and fell flat on the floor. 92

"What happened?" Paige asked while laughing. 98

Faith wanted only to go into a large hole and hide. 109

The bell rang and Faith darted out the door. She 119
was happy to finally be going home. But up ahead, 129
Faith saw Paige playing catch. 134

"Maybe I should cross the street," she thought. But 143
there was no time. A huge truck was coming. It was 154
going way too fast. Then she saw Paige in the street 165
getting her ball. Paige didn't see the truck coming. 174
There was no time to waste. Faith quickly grabbed 183
Paige and pulled her safely up onto the sidewalk. 192

"You saved my life!" Page cried. "Why?" 199

"I just didn't think about it," Faith answered. "I just 209
did what I had to do." 215

They were both quiet for a minute. 222

Then Paige said, "I'd like to have you, Faith, as 232
a friend." 234

A Friend in Need 4

by Karen Riley 7

Johnny had been in his school for two weeks. He 17
was doing well with his work. He was sitting in front 29
of the classroom. This helped him hear the teacher. 38
She tried to look at him when she was talking. This 49
helped him read her lips. But none of the children 60
had come up to play with him. Johnny thought they 70
didn't want to be his friend because he was different. 80
Johnny was hearing impaired. 82

Then one day Edgar asked Johnny to eat lunch 91
with him. Edgar spoke slowly. He used his hands to 101
sign words like "eat" and "ball." Johnny was happy to 111
have a chance to talk with a friend. 119

The next day Edgar did something brave. He 127
talked to his friends about Johnny. He told them how 137
"cool" Johnny was. He told them all they had to do 148
was talk slowly and look right at Johnny. If Johnny 158
could see their lips, he could read them. Edgar also 168
showed them some sign language. 173

At lunch, Edgar and his friends went to sit with 183
Johnny. They asked Johnny if he wanted to play ball 193
with them after lunch. 197

Before they went to play ball, Johnny thanked 205
Edgar. It took courage for Edgar to introduce Johnny 214
to all of his friends. 219

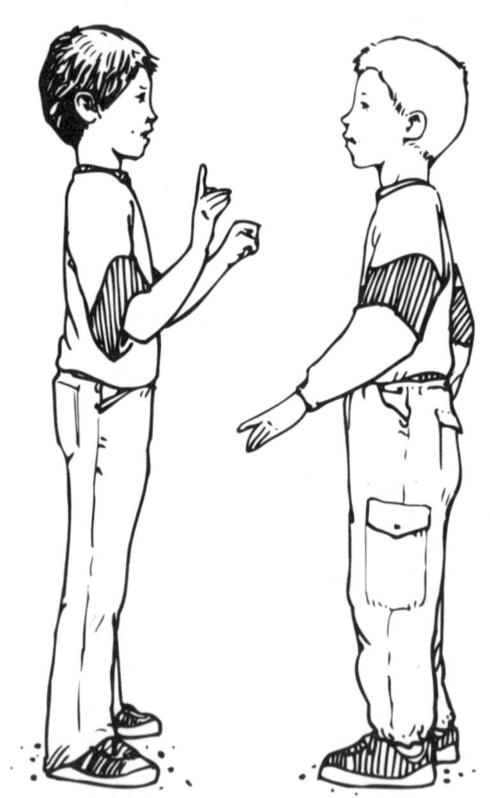

Up a Tree 3

by Emily Jones 6

Dear Aunt Jane, 9

You won't believe what happened last week! I 17
saved my cat's life. Let me tell you all about it. 28

Last week I was sitting outside reading a book. 37
Suddenly, I heard a shrill scream. Only it wasn't the 47
kind of scream a person would make. It seemed more 57
like a small animal's scream. 62

I trotted into the field near our house and looked 72
up the tree. There was little DeeDee, my cat! She 82
seemed to be crying. 86

DeeDee was sitting on a branch. 92

"DeeDee, leap down!" I called. But she seemed 100
afraid to move. When she did move, she almost 109
slipped off the branch! I had to help. 117

Slowly, I climbed up the tree. I had to be careful 128
not to fall. At last I reached DeeDee on the branch. I 140
could see that her foot was hurt. It had a tiny piece 152
of wood, or a splinter, in it. I grabbed her with one 164
hand. We both got down the tree safely. 172

Dad helped me get the wood out of DeeDee's 181
injured paw. He said it was brave of me to save my 193
cat! I agree! 196

Your loving niece, 199

Emily 200

Helen Keller: A Woman of Courage 6

by Lee Davis 9

To talk about courage is to talk about Helen Keller. 19
Although Helen couldn't see or hear, she still showed 28
a lot of courage. Helen did more than many people 38
with hearing and sight ever do. 44

Early Years 46

Helen Keller was born in 1880 in Alabama. When 55
she was a baby, she got sick. She got better, but she 67
couldn't see or hear anymore. Her world was now 76
dark and silent. 79

Helen's teacher was Anne Sullivan. Anne thought 86
she could teach Helen to read and write. Helen 95
learned to spell because Anne would spell words in 104
Helen's hand. Helen also learned to read in Braille. 113
Braille is raised dots that represent letters. People 121
feel them with their fingers. Helen also learned to 130
read lips with her fingers. From this, Helen spoke her 140
first sentence. 142

Later Years 144

Helen graduated with honors from Radcliffe College 151
in 1904. She wrote a book, *The Story of My Life*, 162
when she was in college. 167

Helen went all over the world. She spoke about 176
helping those who couldn't see or hear. She wrote two 186
more books. She started many groups to help others. 195
Helen Keller died in 1968. She was 87 years old. 205

Think about the courage Helen Keller showed. She 213
wouldn't give up. She fought to reach her goals. How 223
will you show your courage? 228

Into the Deep 3

by William Wertz 6

Two men were inside a strange submarine. It was 15
called a *bathyscaphe.* It was small. It had thick steel 25
walls. It had small windows. The men could look out. 35
They were explorers. 38

Lieutenant Don Walsh was employed by the U.S. 46
Navy. Jacques Piccard was a French scientist. Other 54
men had explored the land, but no one had explored 64
the deep oceans. They both enjoyed studying the 72
ocean and wanted to explore the bottom of the 81
deepest ocean. 83

They started to dive. They sank deeper and deeper. 92
It got dark. Soon it was black as night. Then the sub 104
shook and—*bump!* They were on the bottom. 112

Their instruments read 35,800 feet. More than 119
six miles of water were on top of them. They 129
were deeper than man had ever gone before! How 138
amazing! 139

While they were down there, they turned on a big 149
light. They explored the ocean floor. They saw an 158
odd fish. It was flat. Its eyes were on the same side 170
of its head. It lived on the bottom. 178

Walsh and Piccard had proved two things. Things 186
were living in the deepest part of the ocean. And men 197
could go there to see them! 203

Glenn Cunningham: He Wouldn't Quit 5

by Rosalie Koskimaki 8

Glenn Cunningham loved to run. He could run 16
faster than his friends. When he was a boy, Glenn 26
wanted to be the fastest runner in the world. 35

One day, there was a big fire at Glenn's school. 45
Glenn got trapped inside the school. He was burned 54
very badly. 56

His legs were hurt worse than anything else. The 65
doctors told him that he would never walk again. 74

But Glenn wouldn't believe the doctors. He made a 83
choice that he would walk and run again. 91

Glenn stayed in bed for a year. All he thought 101
about was walking. When he got stronger, he tried to 111
walk. It hurt, but he didn't care. He kept trying. 121

At last he could walk. What a surprise for the 131
doctors! And then he started to run. Soon he could 141
run faster than all his friends. 147

Glenn began to run in races. He was a *miler.* That 158
means the races he ran were a mile long. He could 169
run the mile faster than anyone else. He became the 179
fastest miler in the United States. Later, he became 188
the fastest miler in the world! 194

Glenn didn't care if his legs hurt him, and he didn't 205
care how they looked. He knew he had the fastest 215
legs in the world. 219

Glenn Cunningham enjoyed running many races 225
and even won an Olympic silver medal. He's not 234
the fastest miler in the world anymore. But he's still 244
remembered. 245

Put It Back 3

by Michelle Wong 6

Simon couldn't believe his eyes. Paul had just 14
taken Tina's lunch bag. Simon stood still for a minute. 24
He didn't know what to do. He had to make a choice. 36

The morning passed slowly. Simon kept one eye 44
on Paul as he worked. "What are you looking at?" 54
Paul asked Simon. 57

"I guess I'm looking at you," Simon answered. "I 66
saw you take Tina's lunch. Was it a mistake?" 75

"Tina bugs me all the time," Paul whispered. "It 84
serves her right. You won't tell on me, will you?" 94

Simon pretended not to listen. 99

Minutes later, the recess bell clanged noisily. *It* 107
would be a good time for Paul to put Tina's lunch 118
back, Simon thought. 121

"Will you quit looking at me!" Paul yelled. "It's just 131
a lunch!" 133

"But it's Tina's lunch," Simon yelled back. A crowd 142
of boys gathered around Simon and Paul. 149

Simon's mouth felt parched. His hands quaked. 156

"What are you going to do?" Paul taunted. "Are 165
you going to tell on me?" 171

"Guess I'll leave it up to you, Paul," Simon said. "If 182
you put Tina's lunch back, I won't tell." 190

The recess bell rang, and the boys went back 199
inside. 200

"Time for lunch," said Mr. James. 206

Simon was the last person to get in line and the 217
last person to sit down. Simon walked by Tina on the 228
way to his seat. She was eating her lunch. 237

Ski Hero  2

by Mike Neigoff 5

Lee clung to his ski poles and looked at the scene 16
in front of him down the hill. 23

"What are you waiting for?" Debbie asked. "It's not 32
very steep." 34

"I know," Lee said. He was shivering because he 43
was afraid. *This was a mistake,* he thought. *Why did* 53
I agree to come on this class ski trip? Lee just knew 65
he would fall down. 69

"I'm off!" Debbie squealed. 73

"Look at her go!" said Bob. "It looks scary." 82

Lee looked at him. Bob did not look happy. Bob 92
was as scared as Lee! Lee decided not to show that 103
he was afraid too. 107

"You won't get hurt," Lee said to Bob. "Even if you 118
fall, the snow is soft." 123

"Maybe I can take off these skis and walk down," 133
Bob said. 135

Lee told himself that Bob was being illogical. It 144
was only a little hill. He forgot how scared he was 155
himself. 156

"Come on," Lee said. "I'll go down with you. Just 166
remember what Mr. Kim, our ski teacher, taught us." 175

"Let's go!" he yelled and pushed off. He was skiing! 185
And he was still on his feet! 192

Bob slid up to him. 197

"I fell once," he said, panting. "But it was fun! I'm 208
glad you made me do it." 214

Lee grinned. He was never going to tell anyone 223
how scared he had been. 228

"Let's go back and do it again!" he shouted. 237

The Jamestown Settlement 3

by Rebecca Douglas 6

The Settlers 8

In 1607, 104 people sailed from London, England, to 17
Virginia. They started a new settlement. They named 25
it Jamestown, after King James I of England. This was 35
the first lasting English settlement in North America. 43

People came to America for many reasons. One of 52
the reasons they came to Jamestown was to find gold. 62

But the settlers soon ran into hard times. We know 72
that many people got sick. They had very little food. 82
Most of the time they were looking for gold. Little 92
time was used for farming. 97

The Powhatans 99

When the English people arrived in Jamestown, 106
they settled next to the Powhatans who already 114
lived there. The Powhatans were Native Americans. 121
There were 1200 Powhatans living there at that time. 130
The Powhatans and the settlers all suffered from a 139
shortage of food. 142

Help Arrives 144

Finally the settlers and the Powhatans received 151
help from England. Captain John Smith came to 159
Jamestown. He showed the settlers how to work 167
their farms to grow food. He ruled that everyone 176
had to farm the land for four hours a day. Thomas 187
West also helped the settlers and brought needed 195
goods to Jamestown. John Rolfe set up businesses 203
in Jamestown to help the settlers. He later married 212
Pocahontas, a daughter of the Powhatan chief. 219

Life became more pleasant in the Jamestown 226
settlement. The English were now able to work and 235
build their new homes. 239

Aunt Maria 2

by Claire Arillo 5

My name is Michael, and I am ten years old. I 16
have a sister named Carmen, who is seven. Carmen 25
and I live with my mother and my Aunt Maria. 35
Our house is close to a river where I like to sit and 48
read. Sometimes Aunt Maria sits with me and tells 57
me stories about life in her home country in South 67
America. She tells me about all the things she did 77
when she was a young girl. 83

I like to hear about Aunt Maria's work on the 93
banana boats. The banana business is a big business 102
with a lot of bananas being shipped from South 111
America to the United States. When my family asked 120
Aunt Maria to come live with us, she sailed here on 131
one of those boats. 135

It must have been hard for Aunt Maria because 144
she never spoke English before coming to the United 153
States. Now she goes to school to learn English, and 163
my sister and I help her with her homework. 172

Aunt Maria is happy because she will soon 180
become a citizen of the United States. But before 189
she becomes a citizen, she must first study and learn 199
about this country. Then, when she passes a test, 208
she will become a citizen. Aunt Maria can't wait until 218
that important day arrives. When it does, we will 227
celebrate with a big party. It will be a happy day for 239
all of us, but especially for Aunt Maria. 247

A New Name 3

by Cal Homer 6

Raizel waited in the long line with Mama. They had 16
just left the ship, which finally docked in New York 26
City. Their trip had been long and hard. Each week 36
at sea, Raizel had felt weaker and weaker. 44

"Smile, my little lamb," Mama said sweetly. "Papa 52
will pick us up soon. He will take us to our new home." 65

Raizel knew little about her new home. She only 74
knew it would be better than her old one. Life had 85
become very hard back in Europe. 91

The line moved forward. Raizel held Mama's hand 99
tightly. 100

"Keep calm, my lamb," Mama sighed. "Just stay by 109
my side." 111

At last they were at the head of the line. A tall 123
man sat behind a large desk. He looked at Raizel and 134
smiled. 135

"What is your name?" he asked. 141

"Raizel Katz," she answered. 145

"Write your name right here in the book," the man 155
said. Raizel did so. The man looked at it. 164

"Raizel," the man said, "I will give you a new 174
American name. Let's call you Rose." He wrote the 183
new name next to the old one. 190

Raizel looked up at Mama with a worried look. 199

"Mama, I have a new name. But will I still be your 211
little lamb?" 213

"Always," Mama replied, hugging her daughter. 219
"Always." 220

The Big, Shiny Pot 4

by Susan Rudolph 7

On the kitchen table sits a big, shiny pot. It was 18
once used to make tea. My great-grandfather brought 27
it to America when he came from Russia many years 37
ago. He also came with many stories. I pretend that I 48
can still talk to him. I can hear him telling me about 60
sailing from Russia to America. 65

"I sailed to America from far away," he would say. 75
"I was down in the lowest part of the boat. It was 87
called the *steerage*. Hundreds of people were in one 96
room. Life was hard. In the beginning of the trip, we 107
only ate potatoes. Then I was starving because we 116
ran out of potatoes. 120

"One night someone on the top deck sent fruit 129
down to us in steerage. I had never seen a banana 140
before. I tried it. I didn't like it at all. Not knowing 152
how to eat it, I threw away the banana and ate the 164
peel. Then someone taught me how to eat a banana. 174

"On some nights we would talk and sing and have 184
a good time. Other nights we didn't talk at all. But it 196
was all worth it when I got to America. I will never 208
forget the feeling I had when I saw the Statue of 219
Liberty." 220

I like to remember my great-grandfather and his 229
stories. And whenever I look at that big, shiny pot, it 240
reminds me of what he went through to get here. 250

The Secret Railroad 3

by Mark Scheiman 6

It was the middle of the night. John gently shook 16
his wife and child, who were still sleeping. John knew 26
the time was right to leave. 32

"Let's go," he whispered. "It's time." 38

The three arose quickly. Having gone to sleep 46
in their clothes, they were already dressed. John 54
peeked out of the slave shack to make sure no one 65
was watching. Then the three sneaked through 72
the large cotton field. They were careful not to 81
make any noise. 84

"Daddy, where's the train?" the boy asked. 91

"Hush," John whispered. "We'll talk later." 97

The three finally made their way through the long 106
field. Now they hid on the side of the road. 116

"Will the train stop here?" the boy asked. 124

John smiled. "There is no train, son." 131

The boy looked puzzled. "That's wrong, Daddy," he 139
said. "You told me we were going on a railroad." 149

"It's a secret railroad, son," John explained. "Few 157
people know about it. Nothing is written down. 165
There aren't any trains, rails, or tracks. We must 174
walk, not ride." 177

Just then a woman came quietly down the road. 186

"Here's our conductor," John said. "She'll lead us on 195
our way to the North and to freedom." 203

Soon all four had disappeared into the dark of 212
the night. 214

Cricket 1

by Susan Day 4

I really like cricket. When I feel sad, cricket makes 14
me happy. Who is this cricket? It sounds strange. 23
It isn't a person or an animal. It is like baseball. 34
When I lived in Pakistan, my friends and I played 44
it all the time. My best friend Saleem and I played 55
cricket every day after school. We even got up early 65
sometimes and played before school. We became 72
good players and our team was number one. 80

A few years ago my family moved to America. 89
When I first came here, many things were hard for me, 100
especially because I didn't speak English. The hardest 108
thing for me was missing my best friend Saleem. But 118
I slowly began to make new friends, and now I like 129
them very much. They taught me many new things. 138
Speaking to them helped me learn English quickly. 146

Now it's very easy for me. They showed me some 156
great books and new music. I taught them how to play 167
cricket. Some of them have become good players. 175

Last year I got a big surprise. Saleem and his 185
family moved to America! Can you guess what we do 195
every day after school and sometimes before school? 203
Yes, that's right—we play cricket! But now we play 213
with our American friends. 217

Playing cricket makes me happy. And playing with 225
my best friend Saleem makes me happiest of all. 234

Welcome to Liberty 3

by Andy Strauss 6

Have you ever been to the Statue of Liberty? No? 16
Well, let's go! 19

Getting to Lady Liberty 23

First you get on a boat. The boat goes from New 34
York City to Liberty Island. Soon Lady Liberty rises 43
in front of you. You can see her face, her crown, and 55
her torch. She is made of copper, which is now green. 66
This is the sight that many immigrants saw when 75
they first came to America. Lady Liberty gives you a 85
warm welcome just like the one she gave them. 94

The boat lands, and you get off. You go down the 105
long dock and enter the park. 111

The trees in the park hide Lady Liberty. You follow 121
the groups of people and get closer to the statue. 131
Suddenly, there she is, big as big can be. And way up 143
there is her crown. That is where you are going! 153

Inside Lady Liberty 156

You enter the fort below the statue. You look up. 166
Once inside all you can see are stairs! You climb into 177
the statue. You see the inside of her copper robe. You 188
see the many iron beams that hold her together. 197

You climb and look. There's her arm holding the 206
book. There's her other arm, the one that holds the 216
torch. You climb a few more stairs. You are now 226
inside her crown. You look through the windows at 235
New York City and the boats in the water. Now you 246
are the one welcoming the people. You and Lady 255
Liberty! 256

The Fourth of July 4

by Kelly Coleman 7

Today is the Fourth of July. My family is having 17
a picnic with our neighbors. I'm so glad that you are 28
joining us this afternoon. Our friends who come to 37
this picnic think of the Fourth of July as more than 48
a birthday party for America. We also celebrate the 57
many different kinds of people who live here in the 67
United States. It seems that almost every person here 76
came from a different country. 81

I have never tasted anything as good as the food 91
people bring here for our picnic. Sometimes it's 99
strange, but it's always good! Come, I'll gladly take 108
you around. 110

Meet Manny, my best friend. He was born in 119
Peru. His dad makes the best chili. It's very hot, so 130
eat it slowly. Do you hear that music? Tony and 140
Olivia brought tapes from Italy. They came to the 149
United States only last year. There is Miss Hall. Her 159
grandmother moved here from France a long time 167
ago. Miss Hall brought Fifi, her dog, to the picnic. 177

Would you like more candy? My mother's friend 185
brought it from Japan. Some candy in Japan is made 195
with beans. It is very sweet. She and her family 205
moved here from Japan last summer. 211

See what I mean? This is what the United States 221
is all about: one country that's made up of many 231
different people. How fun! Happy birthday, United 238
States of America! 241

Bill Pickett: First African-American 5
Cowboy 6

by Derrick Lewis 9

Bill Pickett was born in 1870 to parents who were 19
once slaves. He grew up on a small ranch in Texas. 30
Pickett took care of the animals. He helped plant 39
the crops. 41

Pickett loved to ride horses and was a great rider. 51
Pickett rode as well as most cowboys. He felt at 61
home on the back of a good horse. People came from 72
miles away to look at him ride. They asked him to 83
train their horses. 86

Pickett also loved the rodeo. He liked to watch the 96
cowboys ride and herd cows. Pickett wanted to be 105
in the rodeo, too, but African Americans were not 114
permitted to ride in rodeos then. 120

Pickett couldn't ride in a rodeo, but he could work 130
for one. He helped cowboys take care of their horses. 140
He cleaned horse stalls. He did anything he could just 150
to be at the rodeo. 155

When he wasn't working, Pickett practiced tricks 162
with the horses, and he also roped cows. Soon 171
Pickett was more talented than the cowboys in 179
the show. 181

When the owners of The Wild West Rodeo noticed 190
how good Pickett was, they asked him to be its star. 201
People from all over came to see Pickett. The king 211
and queen of England even watched him perform. 219
Everyone agreed that Pickett was one of the best 228
rodeo riders ever! 231

The Same Name Mystery 4

by Tina W. Ziegler 8

David liked to make new friends and solve 16
mysteries. One morning David noticed some new 23
children on the playground. *I hope one of those boys* 33
is in my class, he thought. *It's fun meeting new* 43
people. 44

One boy walked into David's classroom. The 51
teacher asked the boy to write his name on the 61
board. 62

The new student wrote the words *Nguyen Tuan.* 70
At home David told his brother Mike about the 79
new boy. 81

"We have a new student too," said Mike. "His name 91
is Nguyen Dinh. That's strange! They both have the 100
same first name." Mike scratched his head. 107

Their sister Ellen told the family about her 115
new friend. "Her name is Nguyen Lien. She's from 124
Vietnam." 125

David and Mike stared at each other. "Three new 134
people with the same first name! Are they related?" 143
David said. 145

"It's time to play detective," his mother said. 153

David had a hard time falling asleep that night. 162
Questions sprang into his head. 167

Maybe Nguyen *is a common name in Vietnam,* he 176
thought. *But three new people named Nguyen?* 183

The next morning, David dashed over to say hello 192
to Nguyen Tuan. "I'd like you to meet my brother and 203
sister," Nguyen Tuan said to David. "This is Nguyen 212
Dinh and Nguyen Lien." 216

Now David was confused! Nguyen Tuan smiled. 223
"In my country, names are written in the opposite 232
order of American names. The family name is first, 241
and the personal name is last." 247

David laughed. "Thanks for solving the mystery. 254
I hope we can be friends." 260

Name ______________________ Date ____________

Focus

A noun is a word that names a person, place, thing, or idea.

Practice

Read each sentence. Circle the nouns.

1. My friends have cats.
2. Claude has three pens and two erasers.
3. People like to swim in the pool and the lake.
4. The girls saw many animals at the zoo.

Apply

Read each sentence. Circle the nouns.

1. The girl has a balloon.
2. People have lunch at the park.
3. The sun is hot.
4. The boy sees fish swimming in the water.

Name ______________________ Date __________

Focus

A proper noun names a *certain* person, place, thing, or idea. Your first and last names are examples of proper nouns. Proper nouns start with a capital letter.

Practice

Read each sentence. Circle the proper noun in each.

1. The family moved from Mexico to Texas.
2. José's birthday is in May.
3. Mr. Kim sailed in a boat on Saturday.

Apply

Read each sentence. Circle the proper nouns and underline the common nouns in each.

1. Chan plays baseball for the Tornadoes.
2. Rex is a dog that can do many tricks.
3. Mark and Lee go to Corner Park every Friday to play tennis.
4. Grace has a job at Sam's Store.

Name ______________________ Date ____________

Focus

An action verb is a word that shows action. It names something that a person or thing can do.

Practice

Read each word. Circle all of the action verbs.

apple	cry	run	girl
tree	dish	eat	fly

Apply

Read each sentence. Underline the action verb. Then draw a picture to show the action.

1. Kim walks her dog.

2. I sleep in my bed.

3. Dad cooks dinner.

Name ______________________ Date ____________

Focus

An **action verb** names something a person or thing can do.

Practice

Read each sentence. Circle the action verb or verbs in each.

1. The artist paints a picture.
2. Climb the ladder.
3. Can you count to one thousand?
4. Listen to her sing the song.
5. Please talk quietly in the library.

Apply

Underline each sentence that has an action verb. Circle the action verb.

1. The man dug with a shovel.
2. The fish swims fast.
3. I was happy today.
4. The boy kicked the ball.
5. It is cold outside.

Name ______________________ Date ____________

Focus

Sometimes there are two verbs in a sentence. When this happens, the first verb is usually a helping verb. A helping verb tells when something is happening or has happened.

Practice

Underline the main verb. Circle the helping verb.

1. I have eaten an apple.
2. The baby was crying.
3. We are playing a game.
4. She has written a letter.

Apply

Read the paragraph below. Circle the helping verbs.

Anna's birthday is next week. She will throw a birthday party. I have already bought Anna a present. We will play games, watch a movie, and eat cake. Do you like birthday parties?

Name ______________________ Date __________

Focus

A linking verb joins, or connects, parts of a sentence to make it complete.

Practice

Read each sentence. Circle the helping verbs. Underline the linking verbs.

1. These fish are blue.
2. The shark is very big.
3. My sisters and I were swimming in the sea.
4. The water was cold.

Apply

Read the story below. Underline the linking verbs. Circle the helping verbs.

There are six fish in my aquarium. The fish are swimming fast. Fluffy is my cat. Fluffy is watching the fish swim. I have told Fluffy that these fish are not for dinner!

Name ____________________ Date __________

Focus

The **subject** is who or what a sentence is about.

Practice

Read each sentence. Underline the subject in each.

1. My mother is working at the bank.
2. The plants are growing.
3. The lake is frozen.
4. Susie is eating ice cream.
5. I won the race!

Apply

Read each sentence. Write a subject to complete each sentence. Use a word from the box.

babies	Steve
school	dog
lunch	

1. My ________ is closed today.
2. The ________ chased my cat.
3. ________ is sick today.
4. ________ was yummy!
5. ________ sleep in cribs.

Name ______________________________ Date ____________

Focus

The **subject** tells who or what the sentence is about; the **predicate** tells what the subject is or does.

Practice

Read each sentence. Underline the subject. Circle the predicate.

1. Alex walked to the park.
2. We watched a movie about lions.
3. The desk is messy.

Apply

Write a sentence to describe each picture. Underline your subject and circle your predicate.

1. 

____

3. 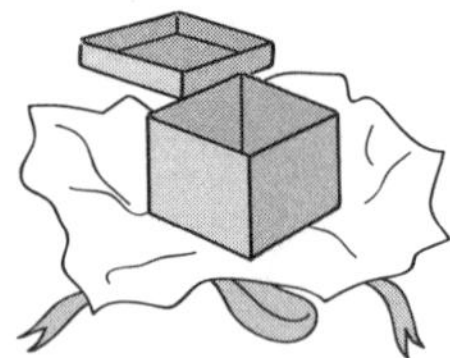

____

2. 

____

4. 

____

Name ______________________ Date ____________

Focus

Every sentence begins with a capital letter.

Practice

Read each sentence. Underline the word that should begin with a capital letter, and change the lowercase letter to a capital letter.

1. we made homemade ice cream. ________
2. look before you cross the street. ________
3. sam slept late. ________
4. everyone liked the cookies. ________
5. the car is in the parking lot. ________

Apply

Read the paragraph. Circle each word that should be capitalized.

i have a dog named Mac. she is white with black spots. she is my best friend. we go everywhere together. yesterday we went to the park and played with a ball all afternoon. tomorrow we are going to the beach. mac loves to swim!

Name ______________________________ Date ___________

Focus

Capital letters are used in many places. One place capital letters are used is at the beginning of a sentence. Another place they are used is in proper nouns.

Practice

Read each sentence. Capitalize the correct letters.

1. today, my class is going to the san diego zoo. ___________
2. mrs. jones is our teacher. ___________
3. danny likes the monkeys the best. ___________
4. my friend jim and I like the african lions the best. ___________

Apply

Read the paragraph. Circle each word that should be capitalized.

last sunday, i went to the philadelphia museum. i saw many fun paintings there. aunt julia liked the painting of french dancers in pink costumes. my favorite painting was of a spanish horse.

Name ______________________ Date ____________

Focus

A **complete sentence** has a subject and a predicate. An **incomplete sentence** is missing a subject or a predicate.

Practice

Circle *C* for a complete sentence. Circle *I* for an incomplete sentence.

1. It rained yesterday. C I
2. Just before the storm, Tom. C I
3. Two cakes and a pie. C I
4. The truck is red. C I

Apply

Circle the words that correctly complete each sentence.

1. Pumas	are members of the cat family.	running fast in the forest.
2. A puma	big and strong.	can live in a hot area.
3. The mountain lion	is another name for the puma.	same as a puma.
4. A puma	speed helps it escape danger.	has sharp teeth.

Name ______________________ Date __________

Focus

A **complete sentence** has a subject and a predicate. An **incomplete sentence** is missing a subject or a predicate. An incomplete sentence is called a **sentence fragment.**

Practice

Write *C* for complete sentence. Write *F* for sentence fragment.

1. Bright red roses in my garden. ____
2. The roses need plenty of sun. ____
3. They also plenty of water. ____

Apply

Rewrite the sentence fragments to make them complete sentences.

1. Tomorrow at school.

   ____

2. In the park with my friends.

   ____

3. Dinner with my family.

   ____

Name ______________________ Date ____________

Focus

A **declarative sentence** makes a statement. An **imperative sentence** gives a command or directions.

Practice

Circle *D* if the sentence is declarative. Circle *I* if the sentence is imperative.

1. Give me the paper. D I
2. Put on your coat. D I
3. I have a coat. D I

Apply

Write two declarative and two imperative sentences of your own.

1. Declarative ______________________
2. Declarative ______________________
3. imperative ______________________
4. imperative ______________________

Name ______________________ Date __________

Focus

An **interrogative sentence** asks a question. It ends with a question mark. An **exclamatory sentence** shows strong feeling. It ends with an exclamation mark.

Practice

Read each sentence. Add the correct end mark.

1. When does the party start
2. That elephant is huge
3. Did you leave it behind
4. Look out
5. Did we win

Apply

Read the paragraphs. Insert end marks where they belong.

What sharp teeth sharks have If they lose a tooth, can they grow another one

It's amazing that sharks can weigh as much as three elephants Have you ever seen a shark

Name ______________________ Date ____________

Focus

A **proper noun** names a certain person, place, thing, or idea. The first letter of a proper noun begins with a capital letter.

Practice

Read each sentence. Circle the proper nouns.

1. The Golden Gate Bridge is in California.
2. Davy Crockett was an explorer.
3. Sara's birthday is in June.
4. We went to Paris and then to Rome.

Apply

Rewrite each sentence. Capitalize the proper nouns.

1. Is the pacific ocean the deepest ocean?

   ____

2. orville and wilbur wright made the first airplane in 1903.

   ____

3. neil armstrong was the first person to walk on the moon.

   ____

Name ______________________ Date ____________

Focus

People's titles begin with a capital letter. People's initials are capital letters.

Practice

Rewrite each name and title correctly.

1. president washington ____________
2. k.c. smith ____________
3. mr. juarez ____________
4. dr. kelly ____________

Apply

Rewrite each sentence to correct errors in capitalization.

1. My friend p.j. is in mrs. miller's class.

   ____

2. Ross wrote a report about president abraham lincoln.

   ____

3. K. t. had a meeting with mayor stern.

   ____

Name ______________________ Date __________

Focus

An **adjective** describes a noun and tells what kind, what color, or how many.

Practice

Read each sentence. Circle the adjectives.

1. The water is cold.
2. I am shy when I meet new people.
3. I like crisp, red apples.
4. Jen's new car is purple.

Apply

Choose an adjective for each noun. Draw a picture to match.

_____ tiger	_____ grass
_____ girl	_____ flower

Name ______________________ Date __________

Focus

An **adjective** describes a noun and tells what kind, what color, or how many.

A, an, and *the* are special adjectives. *A* comes before a noun that starts with a consonant sound.

An comes before a noun that starts with a vowel sound. *The* can come before any noun.

Practice

Read each sentence. Circle the adjectives.

1. The baby has a soft, yellow blanket.
2. I was sick yesterday.
3. The dog is wet from his bath.

Apply

Choose an adjective to complete each sentence. Use a word from the word box or a word of your own.

best	brown	funny

1. This is the _____ sandwich I ever ate!
2. The movie was _____.
3. The twins have _____ hair.

Name ______________________ Date ____________

Focus

A **singular noun** names one person, place, or thing. A **plural noun** names more than one person, place, or thing.

Practice

Write the plural for each noun.

1. cake ______________________
2. dog ______________________
3. peach ______________________

Apply

Complete each sentence. Write the plural form of the singular noun next to the line.

1. Jen has two pet __________. *frog*
2. Please wash the __________. *dish*
3. There are three second grade __________. *class*
4. We drove past many __________. *ranch*

Name ______________________ Date __________

Focus

A **singular noun** names one person, place, or thing. A **plural noun** names more than one person, place, or thing.

Practice

Write the plural for each noun.

1. fly ______________
2. baby ______________
3. hoof ______________
4. shelf ______________

Apply

Complete each sentence. Write the plural form of the singular noun next to the line.

1. Marcos and Jamal are my best ______________. *buddy*
2. The police caught the two ______________. *thief*
3. We baked three ______________. *loaf*
4. Reading and jogging are my ______________. *hobby*

Name ______________________ Date __________

Focus

The words *a*, *an*, and *the* are special adjectives called articles.
Use *a* before a noun that begins with a consonant sound.
Use *an* before a noun that begins with a vowel sound.
Use *the* before any noun.

Practice

Circle the word that completes each sentence.

1. Did you see the bird get ____ worm? a an

2. Do you want ____ egg for breakfast? a an

3. Please put ____ dog out. an the

Apply

Write *a* or *an* to complete each sentence.

1. Do you have ____ idea?

2. Is that ____ bank?

3. I have ____ new puppy.

4. Have you ever ridden on ____ elephant's back?

Name ______________________ Date ____________

Focus

A comparative adjective compares two nouns. Add *–er* to the end of an adjective to make it mean "more of" something.
A superlative adjective compares three or more nouns. Add *–est* to the end of an adjective to make it mean "the most of" something.

Practice

Complete the chart.

	Comparative	Superlative
clean		
fast		

Apply

Choose two comparative adjectives and two superlative adjectives from the chart. Use each one in a sentence.

1. ______________________

2. ______________________

3. ______________________

4. ______________________

Name ______________________ Date ____________

Focus

The days of the week begin with a capital letter.
The months of the year begin with a capital letter.

Practice

Circle each word that should be capitalized.

1. This year school begins on wednesday, september 5.
2. I have to go to the dentist next thursday.
3. My birthday is friday, february 4.

Apply

Rewrite each sentence using correct capitalization.

1. On monday, we went to a museum.

____

2. On tuesday, Molly and Joe went to the zoo.

____

3. What did you do on thursday and friday?

____

4. june is my favorite month!

____

Name ______________________ Date __________

Focus

The names of cities and states begin with a capital letter.

Practice

Underline the word(s) that should be capitalized.

1. My grandmother lives in dallas, texas.
2. The capital of florida is tallahassee.
3. The smallest state in the united states is rhode island.
4. The largest city in california is los angeles.

Apply

Answer the questions.

1. Where do you live? ______________________

   city state

2. What is the name of another city in your state?

   ____

3. What is the name of another state? ______________________

Name ____________________ Date ____________

Focus

Commas separate items listed in a series.

Practice

Insert commas in the proper place.

1. Spain Portugal and France are countries in Europe.
2. My friends are Ivan Sally Josh and Omar.
3. I play soccer on Monday Wednesday and Friday.

Apply

Rewrite each sentence, placing commas in the proper places.

1. Sharks whales and fish live in the ocean.

   ____

2. Steve ate eggs toast and oatmeal for breakfast.

   ____

3. Please feed the dog make your bed and wash the dishes.

   ____

4. I found two dimes a quarter and five pennies in my bag.

   ____

Name ______________________ Date ____________

Focus

Commas separate items in a series.

Practice

Put commas where they belong.

1. There are apples oranges and pears in the fruit basket.
2. We drove through Dallas Austin and San Antonio.
3. Every morning I get dressed eat breakfast brush my teeth and make my bed.

Apply

Write two sentences for each topic given.

1. Write two sentences telling things you did today.

____

____

2. Write sentences naming three people you played with today.

____

____

Name ______________________ Date __________

Focus

The **subject** of a sentence is who or what the sentence is about.
The **verb** describes the action.
The **subject** and **verb** must match. Both must be singular or both plural.

Practice

Underline the subject and the verb. Tell if they are singular or plural.

1. The children are walking the dog.
2. Katie has a new watch.
3. I have four pencils.

Apply

Circle the correct verb to complete each sentence.

1. The dishes ____ dirty.	is	are
2. Susie and Max ____ their dog.	feeds	feed
3. The baby ____ in the afternoon.	naps	nap

Name ______________________ Date ____________

Focus

A singular subject must have a singular verb.
A plural subject must have a plural verb.

Practice

Write the correct verb (*is* or *are*) to complete each sentence.

1. The wind ____ blowing hard.
2. The clothes ____ clean.
3. The city ____ huge.

Apply

Circle the correct verb to complete each sentence.

1. This book (is/are) my favorite.
2. We (was/were) late to the show.
3. The letters (has/have) arrived.
4. The friends (talks/talk) at lunch.
5. The dog (chases/chase) the cat.

Name ______________________________ Date ____________

Focus

If two words are put together to form one word, it is called a contraction. An apostrophe (') takes the place of letters that are taken out.

Practice

Match each contraction with the two words that make it up.

1. don't a. we are

2. we're b. he is

3. he's c. do not

4. I'll d. I will

Apply

Circle the contraction in each sentence. Write the two words that make up the contraction.

1. Anita didn't want to go swimming.

2. I'm in the second grade.

3. Do they know we're here?

4. She's running in a race tomorrow.

Name ________________________________ Date ______________

Focus

Contractions make writing sound more like a conversation.
A contraction may be formed by putting together a verb and the word *not*.
A contraction may be formed by combining a pronoun and a verb.

Practice

Circle the correct contraction in each sentence below.

1. Greenland (isn't / don't) a continent.
2. There (won't / aren't) a lot of people living in Greenland.
3. Hawaii (wasn't / weren't) a state until 1959.

Apply

Write the contractions for the boldfaced words in each sentence below.

1. **I am** going to Arizona in April. ____________________
2. **I have** never been to the Southwest. ____________________
3. I know **she is** going to invite me to her party. ____________________
4. I asked Mary if **she will** eat lunch with me today. ____________________
5. My favorite dessert **is not** on the menu. ____________________

Name ______________________ Date __________

Focus

Pronouns take the place of nouns. A pronoun can be singular or plural, and it must agree in gender, number, and person with the noun it replaces.

Practice

Circle the noun(s) and underline the pronoun(s) in each sentence.

1. Bill went to the store. He bought a hamster.
2. Many frogs are green. They hide easily in heavy vegetation.
3. Susan likes to read stories about animals. She enjoys reading about how they live.
4. My friends and I went to see a show. We had a lot of fun.

Apply

Replace the underlined noun(s) with a pronoun.

1. Anna and Jim went to the zoo. ______________
2. Anna wanted to see the lizards. ______________
3. Lizards blend in with their surroundings. ______________
4. One lizard was lying on a rock. ______________

Name ______________________ Date ____________

Focus

Pronouns take the place of nouns. A pronoun must agree in gender and number with the noun it replaces.

Practice

Replace the underlined noun(s) with a pronoun.

1. Molly gave a book to Susan. ____________
2. Paul bought a present for his grandparents. ____________
3. Jack invited Dylan and me to lunch. ____________
4. Dana's dog was very happy to get a bone. ____________

Apply

Rewrite the sentence by replacing the underlined noun with a pronoun.

1. My parents took my brothers and me to the movies.

   ____

2. My parents, my brothers, and I went to see a movie about lions.

   ____

3. Lions like to hunt and eat smaller animals.

   ____

Name ______________________ Date __________

Focus

Possessive nouns show ownership. To make a noun possessive, add an apostrophe and the letter *s* ('s) to singular nouns and only an apostrophe (') to plural nouns that already end in *s*.

Practice

Underline the possessive noun in each sentence.

1. My mother's car is in the driveway.
2. We need to protect the pandas' habitat.
3. Did you get Bob's message?
4. In October, the trees' leaves turn brown.

Apply

Complete the sentence with a possessive noun using the noun given in parentheses.

1. ______________ (*Eric*) shoes were wet from the snow.
2. The ______________ (*bird*) nest is high up the tree.
3. I am going to my ______________ (*friends*) house today.
4. Mary went to the ______________ (*principal*) office.

Name ______________________________ Date ____________

Focus

Like possessive nouns, **possessive pronouns** show ownership. Unlike possessive nouns, possessive pronouns do not use an apostrophe.

Practice

Circle the possessive noun in each sentence. Then replace it with a possessive pronoun.

1. Last weekend I saw a woodpecker's nest. ____________

2. Joe's mother drove us to the museum. ____________

3. After the game, the girls' uniforms were dirty. ____________

4. Sarah's room was messy, so she cleaned it. ____________

Apply

Complete the paragraph below by using the possessive pronouns from the word box.

their	my	our

Last week, I had a birthday party at _____ house. My friends brought _____ favorite games and toys to share. My brother and I invited everyone to join us in _____ backyard and play ball.

Name ______________________ Date ____________

Focus

Conjunctions join other words or groups of words in a sentence. Three common conjunctions are *and, or,* and *but.*

Practice

Underline the conjunction in each sentence.

1. Geese and other birds fly south for the winter.
2. The teacher is strict but fair.
3. Suzie's father came home from work and played with her.
4. Do you prefer orange juice or lemonade?
5. I wanted to buy a game, but I didn't have enough money.

Apply

Complete each sentence with *and, or,* or *but.*

1. Do you want to go to the movies ______ the park?
2. I love cats, ______ my brother prefers dogs.
3. Anna and I went to the store, ______ we bought candy.
4. My house is old, ______ I love it!
5. Rivers ______ oceans are home to many different fish.

Name ____________________ Date __________

Focus

When two simple sentences are combined they form a **compound sentence.** A compound sentence must always have a conjunction, and a comma is added before it.

Practice

Circle the conjunction. Indicate whether the sentence is a simple sentence or a compound sentence.

1. Hares and squids can change their colors. __________
2. Do you want to eat apples or oranges? __________
3. Dan has a guitar, and he plays it well. __________

Apply

Create compound sentences using the conjunctions *and, or,* or *but.*

1. Roses are red. Violets are blue.

   ____

2. We can walk to the park. We can ride our bikes.

   ____

3. Raul moved to New Mexico. Raul started a new school.

   ____

Name ______________________ Date ____________

Focus

Words with similar meanings are called **synonyms.**

Practice

Match each word from the box to its synonym below.

baby	glad	small	begin	big	tidy

1. tiny ____________

2. happy ____________

3. start ____________

4. infant ____________

5. clean ____________

6. large ____________

Apply

Read each sentence. Write a synonym for the underlined word. Then write a new sentence with the synonym.

1. The fans yelled at the football game.

____

2. My favorite shirt is too small for me now.

____

3. Tara's room is untidy, and she needs to clean it.

____

Name ______________________________ Date ______________

Focus

Words with opposite meanings are called **antonyms.**

Practice

Read each sentence. Circle the pairs of antonyms.

1. An octopus is big, but shellfish are small.
2. Whales are wet, and birds are dry.
3. Owls usually hunt at night, and eagles hunt during the day.

Apply

Write sentences using antonyms to describe the pictures. Use one antonym pair per sentence.

1.  

Jane Molly

____

2.  

Dwayne Steve

____

3. 

Karen Jim

____

4. 

____

Name ______________________ Date __________

Focus

Colons are used to introduce a list and to separate the hour and the minutes when writing the time.

Practice

Read each sentence. Add colons when necessary.

1. Danny woke up at 6 30 today.
2. Then he went to a restaurant to have breakfast two eggs, bacon, toast, and orange juice.
3. In school, he attended all his classes math, science, art, and language arts.
4. At 12 00 Danny had lunch, and at 12 30 he went to recess.
5. After school, Danny and his friends rode their bikes to the park and played several games hide-and-seek, soccer, and football.

Apply

Read the paragraph. Insert colons where they belong.

Today is Amanda's birthday. Her mother invited the following friends to her party Ruth, Patty, Jane, and Trisha. The party will start at 4 00 and end at 6 30. Amanda's mom prepared a lot of snacks pizza, salad, fruit, and lemonade. Amanda is very excited, and she already planned several activities face painting, musical chairs, and playing tag outside.

Name ______________________________ Date ____________

Focus

Colons are used to introduce a list and to separate the hour and the minutes when writing the time.

Practice

Complete the following sentences by inserting colons where they are needed.

1. The class will start promptly at 830. ____________
2. Kate needs the following ingredients from the store flour, eggs, and butter. ____________
3. When we went to the zoo we saw many big animals monkeys, lions, and elephants. ____________

Apply

Write one sentence using time and two sentences that include a list. Insert colons where needed.

1. Time: ______________________________
2. List: ______________________________
3. List: ______________________________

Name ______________________ Date ____________

Focus

In a letter, the first word of a greeting is capitalized, and a comma is placed between the recipient's name and the beginning of the letter. The first word of a closing is capitalized, and a comma is placed between the salutation and the writer's name.

Practice

Read the following word groups. Capitalize the correct letters.

1. dear betty,
2. regards, tom
3. dear mrs. jones,
4. yours, liz

Apply

Rewrite the following word groups with the correct capitalization.

1. dear tonya, ______________________
2. your friend, rose ______________________
3. sincerely, mr. smith ______________________
4. dear ms. clarke, ______________________

Name ______________________________ Date ____________

Focus

In a letter, the first word of a greeting is capitalized, and a comma is placed between the recipient's name and the beginning of the letter. The first word of a closing is capitalized, and a comma is placed between the salutation and the writer's name.

Practice

Underline each word that should be capitalized. Add commas where needed.

1. your friend patrick
2. sincerely ms. niels
3. dear mr. peters
4. best regards taylor

Apply

Rewrite the following word groups, and correct the mistakes.

1. dear, Bridget ______________________________
2. yours truly tom ______________________________
3. love dad, ______________________________
4. dear Mrs. brown ______________________________

Name ______________________________ Date ____________

Focus

Quotation marks are placed around a speaker's exact words. They also go around the titles of stories, poems, and songs.

Practice

Insert quotation marks where needed.

1. My favorite nursery rhyme is Twinkle, Twinkle, Little Star.
2. The teacher said, Open your reading books.
3. Wait for me! shouted my little sister.
4. Did you read the story Little Red Riding Hood?

Apply

Complete the sentence using quotation marks where needed.

1. Molly's guitar teacher always says, ____________________.
2. My favorite story is ____________________.
3. ____________________, said Katie when she came to my birthday party.
4. After Joyce spilled orange juice, she said, ____________________.

Name ______________________ Date __________

Focus

Quotation marks are placed around a speaker's exact words, and they also go around the titles of stories, poems, and songs.

Practice

Insert quotation marks where they are needed.

1. Every time Joey is in the car he asks his father, Are we there yet?

2. Jump! ordered the firefighter.

3. Let's have a picnic down by the lake, suggested Peter.

4. Brian plays Mary Had a Little Lamb on the piano.

Apply

Read the paragraph. Insert quotation marks where they are needed.

Steve's favorite story is The Three Little Pigs. He especially likes the part where the wolf comes to the pig's house and says, Little pig, little pig, let me come in. The pig answers, Not by the hair of my chinny chin chin. The wolf then answers, Then I'll huff, and I'll puff, and I'll blow your house in. Every night, at bed time, Steve asks his mother, Would you please read me the story again?

Name ____________________ Date __________

Focus

A comma comes before the quotation marks at the beginning or end of dialogue.

Practice

Insert commas where needed.

1. The teacher asked "Who wants to bring juice to the party?"
2. "This summer, I want to go to the beach" said Jessica.
3. Roger asked his dad "Can we go to the Natural History Museum?"
4. "Certainly" replied his father.
5. The girl said "There is a cat in the tree!"

Apply

Read the following dialogue. Insert commas where needed.

Kim's mother asked Kim "What do you want to do for your birthday party?"

"I want a party with a clown" replied Kim.

Her mother asked "Do you also want balloons?"

Kim exclaimed "Yes, and I want to invite all my friends!"

"It is going to be a fun party" said Kim's mom.

Name ______________________________ Date ______________

Focus

A comma comes before the quotation marks at the beginning or end of dialogue.

Practice

Insert commas where needed.

1. Amy raised her hand and said "I forgot my pencil today."
2. "Thank you for helping me move this desk" said the teacher.
3. When Tracy saw a spider she screamed "Help!"
4. "You are my best friend" Patty said to Judy.

Apply

Read the following dialogue. Insert commas where needed.

Little Red Riding Hood arrived at her grandmother's house and said "Oh Granny, what big ears you have!"
The wolf replied "All the better to hear you with, my dear."
Little Red Riding Hood said "And what big eyes you have!"
The wolf replied "All the better to see you with, my dear."

Name ________________________ Date ____________

Focus

Adverbs describe verbs by telling us *how, where,* or *when.*

Practice

Underline the verbs and circle the adverbs that describe them.

1. The children played loudly during recess.
2. Kay always does her homework.
3. Stan looked everywhere for his lost dog.
4. Dave plays the piano beautifully.

Apply

Complete each section with an adverb from the word box.

alongside	nearby
daily	
lazily	safely

1. Mike's mother drove ____________.
2. My friend Jasmine lives ____________.
3. Joseph helps ____________ in his house.
4. The sailboat is anchored ____________ the dock.
5. The cat stretched ____________ in front of the fireplace.

Name ____________________ Date __________

Focus

Adverbs describe verbs by telling us *how, where,* or *when.*

Practice

Read the following paragraph. Circle the adverbs and underline the verbs that they describe.

Tony and Eric went to the park yesterday. They were playing loudly on the swings. When Cody arrived, he said, "Let's race!" All three ran quickly. Later, at Cody's house, they went downstairs and played happily the rest of the afternoon.

Apply

Write sentences with the following adverbs.

1. tomorrow: ____________________

2. accidentally: ____________________

3. downstairs: ____________________

4. happily: ____________________

Name ______________________________ Date ____________

Focus

Verbs have different tenses to indicate when an action takes place. The different tense tells us whether an action takes place in the past, present, or future.

Practice

Read each sentence. Underline the verbs. Indicate whether the action takes place in the past, present, or future.

1. The student stood up to the bully. ____________
2. Next year, we will be in third grade. ____________
3. Jane and Trisha are playing checkers. ____________
4. Suzie gave me a set of colored pencils. ____________
5. Jim's mom reads the newspaper. ____________

Apply

Read the paragraph. Indicate whether the action takes place in the past, present, or future.

Today I woke _______ up early. I looked _______ out the window and screamed _______, "It is snowing _______!" My mother said _______, "After breakfast, I will take _______ you outside to play in the snow."

Name ______________________ Date __________

Focus

Verbs have different tenses to indicate when an action takes place. The different tense tells us whether an action takes place in the past, present, or future.

Practice

Read each sentence. Underline the verbs. Indicate whether the action takes place in the past, present, or future.

1. In winter, I wear warm clothes. __________
2. Jill fed the rabbit before going to school. __________
3. Richie will turn eight years old in two weeks. __________
4. I will visit my grandparents in Mexico next year. __________

Apply

Write a sentence with each verb.

1. forgets: ______________________
2. danced: ______________________
3. will play: ______________________
4. is climbing: ______________________

Name ________________________ Date ____________

Focus

A **common noun** names a general person, place, or thing. A **proper noun** names a specific person, place, or thing, and begins with a capital letter.

Practice

Circle the common nouns and underline the proper nouns.

1. In December, Maria and her family will visit her grandparents.

2. Bob and Lee will go to the beach next Sunday.

Apply

Read the following paragraph. Underline the common nouns. Add capital letters to the proper nouns.

Last may, I went with my family to visit new york city. We stayed in a hotel near central park. The first day we went to visit the statue of liberty, near ellis island. Now, ellis island is a museum, but in the past it was the first place in the united states that many immigrants saw. My favorite place in the city was times square because it had a lot of colorful lights.

Name ______________________ Date __________

Focus

An **action verb** is a word that shows action.

Practice

Circle the action verb in each sentence.

1. John Smith sailed from England to Virginia.
2. Trisha received a nice present for her birthday.

Apply

Write sentences to describe the pictures using action verbs.

1. 

____

2. 

____

3. 

____

4. 

____

Name ______________________ Date __________

Focus

There are four sentence types: imperative, interrogative, declarative, or exclamatory.

Practice

Add the correct end mark and indicate the sentence type.

1. Grandma Yelina likes to sing Russian songs to us __________
2. Have you finished your homework __________
3. What a beautiful picture __________

Apply

Write examples of each kind of sentence.

imperative: ______________________________

interrogative: ______________________________

declarative: ______________________________

exclamatory: ______________________________

Name ______________________ Date ____________

Focus

The first word of a **sentence** must be capitalized and a sentence must end with a punctuation mark.

Practice

Place a triple underline under the letter that should be capitalized, and insert the correct end mark after each sentence.

1. my new neighbor is from Panama
2. do you want to bake a cake with me
3. this is so wonderful

Apply

Rewrite the sentences using correct capital letters and end marks.

1. we had a barbecue on Labor Day

   ____

2. would you like to go with me to the movies

   ____

3. watch out

   ____

Name ______________________ Date ____________

Focus

The first word of a sentence, proper nouns, titles, initials, days, months, cities, and states must be **capitalized**.

Practice

Read the sentences. Circle the words that should be capitalized.

1. mr. lewis asked the class to dress up nicely for the party.

2. sam sent julia a card on valentine's day.

3. james and c.j. came to visit us on thanksgiving.

Apply

Rewrite each sentence with correct capitalization.

1. anna came from chicago for the memorial day weekend.

____

2. last may, mr. and mrs. jones traveled to france.

____

Name ______________________________ Date ______________

Focus

Comparative adjectives compare the same quality in two or more nouns or pronouns and usually end with the letters *–er* or *–est.*

Practice

Read the following sentences. Circle the comparative adjectives.

1. Hana is tall, but Tom is taller.
2. My grandmother is the sweetest person I know.
3. The Civil Rights Movement brought a better life and equal rights for African Americans in this country.

Apply

Read the following paragraph. Circle the comparative adjectives.

My dog Lady has three puppies. The smallest one is fluffier than the rest. The oldest one is brown and white. The middle puppy is the cutest. My mother told me to give them away. I said, "No, they will be happier with their mother." My mother agreed, and I kept the young puppies.

Name ______________________ Date ____________

Focus

A **contraction** is formed when two words are put together to make one word connected with an apostrophe.

Practice

Read the following sentences. Underline the contractions. Write the two words that form the contraction.

1. We're ready to go to third grade. ____________
2. Do you think they'll be able to come with us to the movies? ____________
3. I haven't seen the Statue of Liberty yet. ____________
4. I'm happy you'll come to my party. ____________

Apply

Form a contraction with the two words. Write a sentence with the contraction.

1. they are ______________________
2. will not ______________________
3. she is ______________________
4. we will ______________________

Name ______________________ Date ____________

Focus

Possessive pronouns *mine, yours, his, hers, theirs, ours,* and *whose* are used alone. *My, your, his, her, its, our, their,* and *whose* are used to modify a noun.

Practice

Read the following sentences. Underline the possessive pronouns.

1. For my birthday, Dan gave me his favorite comic book.
2. The red shirt is hers, and the blue one is mine.

Apply

Fill the blanks with the correct possessive pronoun.

ours	my	our

This summer, we will visit ____ cousins in Florida. ____ favorite activity is to go swimming. Since we are visiting their place, next year they will visit ____.

Name ______________________________ Date ______________

Focus

An **adverb** is a word that describes a verb or an action. Many adverbs end with the suffix *–ly*.

Practice

Read the following sentences. Underline the verbs and circle the adverbs that describe them.

1. Mr. Jones walked slowly around the block.
2. My neighbor shops weekly at the supermarket.
3. I completely understand this book now.
4. Kyle went downstairs with his dad.
5. We will bike to the park tomorrow.

Apply

Read the following paragraph and circle the adverbs.

Yesterday, Little Miss Muffet sat nicely on a tuffet. She was eating slowly her curds and whey. A spider came behind her and sat quietly beside her. Miss Muffet got frightened, screamed loudly, and ran away.

Name ______________________________ Date ____________

Focus

Verb tense indicates if the action has happened in the past, present, or future.

Practice

Read each sentence. Underline the verbs. Indicate whether the action takes place in the past, present, or future.

1. Sue will play the flute next year. ________
2. Sean decided to stay after school for extra credit. ________
3. Donna teaches her dog tricks. ________

Apply

Write if the actions take place in the past, present, or future.

Humpty Dumpty sat ______ on a wall and fell ______ down. All the King's men said, ______ "We will help ______ you." The King asked, ______ "Can you fix ______ Humpty?"